CIVIL WAR

X-MEN

A

MARVEL COMICS

PRESENTATION

CIVIL WAR

X-MEN

CIVIL WAR: X-MEN #1-4
WRITER: DAVID HINE
PENCILERS: YANICK PAQUETTE
WITH AARON LOPRESTI (#3)
INKERS: SERGE LAPOINTE
WITH JAY LEISTEN (#3)
COLORIST: STEPHANE PERU
LETTERER: VC's RUS WOOTON
COVER ART: JUAN DOE
ASSISTANT EDITOR: SEAN RYAN
ASSOCIATE EDITOR: NICK LOWE
EDITOR: MIKE MARTS

X-FACTOR #8-9
WRITER: PETER DAVID
ARTIST: DENNIS CALERO
COLORIST: JOSE VILLARRUBIA
LETTERER: VC's CORY PETIT
COVER ART: RYAN SOOK
ASSISTANT EDITORS: MOLLY LAZER
& AUBREY SITTERSON
EDITOR: ANDY SCHMIDT

CABLE & DEADPOOL #30-32
WRITER: FABIAN NICIEZA
PENCILER: STAZ JOHNSON
INKERS: KLAUS JANSON
WITH JOHN STANISCI (#32)
COLORIST: GOTHAM
LETTERER: DAVE SHARPE
COVER ART: AMANDA CONNER & PAUL MOUNTS
EDITOR: NICOLE BOOSE

X-MEN CREATED BY STAN LEE & JACK KIRBY

COLLECTION EDITOR
JENNIFER GRÜNWALD

ASSOCIATE EDITOR
SARAH BRUNSTAD

ASSOCIATE MANAGING EDITOR
ALEX STARBUCK

EDITOR, SPECIAL PROJECTS
MARK D. BEAZLEY

VP PRODUCTION
& SPECIAL PROJECTS
JEFF YOUNGQUIST

SVP PRINT, SALES & MARKETING
DAVID GABRIEL

BOOK DESIGNER
DAYLE CHESLER

EDITOR IN CHIEF
AXEL ALONSO

CHIEF CREATIVE OFFICER
JOE QUESADA

PUBLISHER
DAN BUCKLEY

EXECUTIVE PRODUCER
ALAN FINE

CIVIL WAR: X-MEN. Contains material originally published in magazine form as CIVIL WAR: X-MEN #1-4, CABLE & DEADPOOL #30-32 and X-FACTOR #8-9. Second edition. First printing 2016. ISBN# 978-0-7851-9571-9. Published by MARVEL WORLDWIDE, INC., a subsidiary of MARVEL ENTERTAINMENT, LLC. OFFICE OF PUBLICATION: 135 West 50th Street, New York, NY 10020. Copyright © 2016 MARVEL No similarity between any of the names, characters, persons, and/or institutions in this magazine with those of any living or dead person or institution is intended, and any such similarity which may exist is purely coincidental. Printed in the U.S.A. ALAN FINE, President, Marvel Entertainment; DAN BUCKLEY, President, TV, Publishing and Brand Management; JOE QUESADA, Chief Creative Officer; TOM BREVOORT, SVP of Publishing; DAVID BOGART, SVP of Operations & Procurement, Publishing; C.B. CEBULSKI, VP of International Development & Brand Management; DAVID GABRIEL, SVP Print, Sales & Marketing; JIM O'KEEFE, VP of Operations & Logistics; DAN CARR, Executive Director of Publishing Technology; SUSAN CRESPI, Editorial Operations Manager; ALEX MORALES, Publishing Operations Manager; STAN LEE, Chairman Emeritus. For information regarding advertising in Marvel Comics or on Marvel.com, please contact Jonathan Rheingold, VP of Custom Solutions & Ad Sales, at jrheingold@marvel.com. For Marvel subscription inquiries, please call 800-217-9158. Manufactured between 1/22/2016 and 2/29/2016 by R.R. DONNELLEY, INC., SALEM, VA, USA.

10 9 8 7 6 5 4 3 2 1

CIVIL WAR
X-MEN

PREVIOUSLY...

THE MUTANT POPULATION WAS GROWING, AND IN SOME PLACES, THRIVING. THEN M-DAY HAPPENED — AND IN ONE WHITE FLASH, 90% OF THE WORLD'S MUTANTS LOST THEIR POWERS. NOW, MUTANTS ARE AT THEIR LOWEST, WITH ONLY ONE PLACE TO TURN. THE XAVIER INSTITUTE FOR HIGHER LEARNING HAS OPENED ITS GATES TO ALL MUTANTS SEEKING SANCTUARY.

BUT THAT SANCTUARY NOW FEELS MORE LIKE A PRISON...

THE OFFICE OF NATIONAL EMERGENCY HAS ARRIVED AT THE INSTITUTE, BRINGING WITH THEM FIVE MANNED SENTINELS. THEY HAVE COME TO PROTECT THE X-MEN IN THEIR TIME OF NEED. BUT "THE 198" (AS THE REFUGEES NOW CALL THEMSELVES) AND THE O*N*E ARE ALREADY FINDING IT DIFFICULT TO DEAL WITH ONE ANOTHER. TENSIONS ARE HIGH.

MEANWHILE, A DISASTER INVOLVING THE SUPER HERO TEAM KNOWN AS THE NEW WARRIORS HAS SHAKEN THE REST OF THE MARVEL UNIVERSE, IGNITING THE CONTROVERSIAL SUPER HERO REGISTRATION ACT. THE ACT THREATENS TO FORCE ALL SUPER HEROES TO REGISTER THEMSELVES WITH THE GOVERNMENT AND BECOME OFFICIAL EMPLOYEES OF S.H.I.E.L.D. THIS HAS SENT A RIFT THROUGHOUT THE SUPER HERO COMMUNITY, PITTING HERO AGAINST HERO. IRON MAN HAS BEEN LEADING THE PRO-REGISTRATION SIDE, WHILE CAPTAIN AMERICA HAS BEEN LEADING THE OPPOSITION.

THE X-MEN HAVE DECIDED TO REMAIN NEUTRAL UP UNTIL NOW, BUT EVENTS WILL SOON FORCE THEM TO PICK A SIDE, WHETHER THEY WANT TO OR NOT.

X-MEN
A MARVEL COMICS EVENT

CIVIL WAR

SO, TO SUM UP. TWO MEMBERS OF X-FORCE WALTZ INTO THE XAVIER ESTATE AND TAKE AWAY OVER HALF THE INTERNEES, LEAVING A GUARD CRITICALLY INJURED.

THEIR CRAFT OUTRUNS THE PURSUING SENTINEL AND WE HAVE NO IDEA WHERE THEY HAVE GONE.

THEY COULD BE WITH CAPTAIN AMERICA FOR ALL WE KNOW.

I'M SURE YOU'LL AGREE, GENERAL LAZER, THIS WAS NOT THE O*N*E'S FINEST HOUR.

THAT AIRCRAFT WAS CLOAKED AGAINST OUR SURVEILLANCE, AND MY PEOPLE WERE NOT AUTHORIZED TO USE THE FORCE NECESSARY TO CONTAIN THE INMATES.

THE FORCE NECESSARY, GENERAL LAZER? WHAT ARE YOU TRYING TO SAY? LET ME SIMPLIFY THIS SITUATION...

...THE WHITE HOUSE HAS ASKED ME TO OVERSEE A SOLUTION WHICH WILL DEMONSTRATE THAT MUTANTS ARE NOT A MENACE TO SOCIETY.

I'D LIKE TO SEE A JOINT FORCE OF MUTANTS AND SENTINELS WORKING TOGETHER TO BRING IN THE RENEGADES. UNFORTUNATELY, THE MAJORITY PREFER TO REMAIN NEUTRAL.

BUT BISHOP HAS RECRUITED THESE TWO--

MICROMAX AND SABRA. THEY'RE GOOD PEOPLE.

AN ENGLISHMAN AND AN ISRAELI-- IS THAT THE BEST YOU CAN FIND?

I SUPPOSE I CAN ALLOW BISHOP AND HIS RECRUITS TO ASSIST--

I'VE RECOMMENDED THAT BISHOP COMMANDS THIS OPERATION IN THE FIELD.

IT WILL BE GOOD FOR THE PUBLIC TO SEE A MUTANT ACTING AS SHERIFF HERE.

"NONE OF YOU SHOULD HAVE ANY ILLUSIONS HERE. WHAT WE'RE ABOUT TO DO *WILL* PUT US OUTSIDE THE LAW."

WON'T BE THE FIRST TIME.

SOONER OR LATER WE'LL BE GOING UP AGAINST BISHOP AND THE SENTINELS...

...OR EVEN IRON MAN AND OTHER REGISTERED HEROES.

WE KNOW WHAT WE'RE GETTING INTO.

I JUST WANT YOU TO BE SURE.

WE'RE ALL SURE, SCOTT. WE FIND THE 198 BEFORE THEY DO. NO MATTER WHAT.

WE'VE CHOSEN OUR SIDE. WE'RE MUTANTS. WE PROTECT OUR OWN--

--TO THE DEATH.

BOBBY?

WHAT HE SAID.

CIVIL WAR: X-MEN #1 ASPEN VARIANT BY MICHAEL TURNER

X-MEN

A MARVEL COMICS EVENT

CIVIL
WAR

ANY LUCK?

I'M THROUGH. I'VE REACHED CAPTAIN AMERICA.

MY GOD, WHAT *HAPPENED* TO YOU?

WHAT DO YOU WANT, CYCLOPS? THIS IS NOT A GOOD TIME FOR ME.

I WAS TOLD THIS WAS THE SECURE WAY TO CONTACT YOU. I NEED YOUR HELP.

THIS LINE IS FOR SUPERHUMANS WHO WANT TO JOIN US.

I DON'T HAVE TIME TO WASTE TRYING TO PERSUADE YOU DOWN OFF THE FENCE.

I'M NOT ON THE FENCE. TWO NIGHTS AGO, I WATCHED GOOD PEOPLE PUT THEIR LIVES ON THE LINE BECAUSE THEY DON'T LIKE TO SEE MUTANTS IN A CAGE.

I'M BEING TOLD THIS IS WHAT MY COUNTRY WANTS.

I DON'T BELIEVE IT.

YOU'RE WAVING THE FLAG IN MY FACE NOW?

YOU AREN'T THE ONLY ONE WHO'S PRESSED FOR TIME, CAP. THE 198 ARE BEING TRACKED RIGHT NOW BY A TEAM OF SENTINELS AND MUTANTS LED BY *BISHOP.* IF WE DON'T FIND THEM FIRST, WE'RE GOING TO BE PICKING THEM UP IN PIECES. SO JUST TELL ME---

---DO YOU KNOW WHERE THEY ARE?

ARE YOU HAPPY NOW?!

LORELEI SAW THE DOLLS! NOW ALL YOUR MUTANT FRIENDS ARE GOING TO KNOW WHAT YOU DID! THEY'LL NEVER LET YOU NEAR THEM AGAIN!

FILTHY LITTLE FREAK!

FREAK? THAT ISN'T A WORD I'D EXPECT TO HEAR COMING FROM A MUTANT.

I'M NOT A MUTANT.

HE'S THE MUTANT. TWO SEPARATE BRAINS. TWO DIFFERENT PERSONALITIES.

THEN MAYBE I NEED TO TALK TO YOUR BROTHER? DOES IT HAVE A NAME?

IT'S A DROOLING IDIOT. IT DOESN'T NEED A NAME. AND IT CAN'T TALK. YOU NEED SOMETHING, TALK TO ME. I'LL MAKE HIM DO IT--

SSSSSSSS

--IF I FEEL LIKE IT.

IT SEEMS THERE'S A GROUNDSWELL OF OPINION IN FAVOR OF GRANTING THE 198 AN *UNCONDITIONAL* AMNESTY.

SEVERAL HIGH-PROFILE CIVIL RIGHTS GROUPS HAVE QUESTIONED THE LEGALITY OF THEIR DETENTION.

THE SMART MONEY SAYS MUTANTS WILL BE TREATED THE SAME AS OTHER SUPERHUMANS.

THAT MEANS NO MORE *DETENTION.* THEY'LL BE FREE TO GO.

IF I DIDN'T KNOW BETTER I'D SAY YOU *DON'T* WANT TO FIND THE 198.

THEY'VE DONE A PRETTY GOOD JOB OF DISAPPEARING. ALL THEY HAVE TO DO IS STAY OFF THE RADAR UNTIL THE PRESIDENT HAS HIS SAY.

IT WOULD MAKE ALL OUR LIVES A LOT SIMPLER.

SIR, IT'S GENERAL LAZER ON THE SECURE LINE FROM THE PENTAGON.

REALLY? HOW DID YOU FIND THEM, GENERAL?

I HAVE MY METHODS.

STAND BY

X-MEN
A MARVEL COMICS EVENT

CIVIL
WAR

X-MEN

A MARVEL COMICS EVENT

CIVIL WAR

AKKK-- H-UK--HELP ME--!

WHAT IS THIS, LAZER?

IF YOU'RE PLAYING TRICKS--

UKK-- DEE--HE-- UKK--

"--HE *TOUCHED* ME."

WHO WOULD HAVE THOUGHT?

A COUPLE OF BROKEN BONES AND THE BIG TOUGH SOLDIER TURNS INTO A QUIVERING SURRENDER MONKEY.

SSSSS-UKK

IF ALL THE MUTANTS IN THE WORLD HAD ONE NECK--

NO ONE ASKED YOUR OPINION, SQUID BOY.

IF I'D HAD MY WAY THEY'D HAVE CUT YOU OUT OF ME BEFORE I COULD WALK.

KRAK!

"SOMETHING HAPPENED OUT THERE IN THE DESERT.

"WHEN THOSE WEAPONS BLEW, WE ALL SAW HOW CLOSE WE CAME TO GENOCIDE.

"BUT WE SURVIVED. NOBODY DIED.

X-FACTOR
A MARVEL COMICS EVENT

CIVIL
WAR

SO THE X-MEN THINK QUICKSILVER MIGHT SHOW UP IN MUTANT TOWN?

THAT'S WHAT CYCLOPS SAID, SIRYN. HE ALSO SAID PIETRO'S SO DANGEROUS THAT IF WE SEE HIM, WE SHOULD CALL IN THE X-MEN AND LET *THEM* HANDLE IT.

Y'SURE WE'RE TALKING 'BOUT THE SAME SPEEDFEET, JAMIE? I MEAN...

...BACK IN THE DAY, HE WASN'T MY FAVORITE GUY. BUT "DANGEROUS?"

WAK

OW!

?

HE THREW IT.

HARD TO SWALLOW, IS ALL I'M SAYING. MEBBE HE'S BEIN' RAIL-ROADED.

AW, COME ON, GUIDO, LET'S NOT SING SAD SONGS ABOUT THE GUY. IN THE OLD DAYS, YOU WANTED TO TAKE A SWING AT HIM NOW AND THEN AS MUCH AS I DID.

BESIDES, WHY WOULD CYCLOPS LIE TO US?

I DUNNO, GUIDO.

YOU'RE SAYING HE MIGHT?

DUNNO THAT EITHER.

HEY, LAYLA. *THAT'S* A THICK BOOK YOU'RE READING. "HARRY POTTER?"

"ATLAS SHRUGGED."

YEAH, THERE'S A CONVERSATION KILLER.

IS THERE *ANYTHING* THAT KID DOES THAT'S NORMAL, JAMIE?

I SAW HER EATING CHEERIOS AND MILK THE OTHER DAY FOR BREAKFAST. PRETTY NORMAL.

THAT WASN'T MILK. THAT WAS YOGURT MIXED WITH EVIAN WATER.

OH. OKAY, THEN, I GUESS NOT, NO.

NINE ACROSS: "AN UNCOMPLICATED TWO THOUSAND POUNDS."

SIMPLETON.

HEY! YEAH! THANKS FOR THE HELP, MONET.

I WASN'T HELPING YOU, RICTOR. I WAS DESCRIBING YOU.

YOU KNOW, I NEVER THOUGHT IT POSSIBLE THAT JAMESON'S EDITORIALS COULD BE EVEN MORE OBNOXIOUS. I UNDERESTIMATED HIM.

MEANING WHAT, SIRYN?

HE'S CROWING ABOUT THIS "SUPER HERO REGISTRATION ACT." SAYING THE GOVERNMENT'S FINALLY LISTENED TO HIM. THAT THIS IS A "NECESSARY FIRST STEP."

SO?

"SO?" HAVE YOU GIVEN THOUGHT TO THE "NECESSARY SECOND STEP?"

NOT REALLY. I LIVE IN THE MOMENT.

THE NEXT STEP IS SHUTTING US DOWN!

THEY CALL IT "EROSION OF FREEDOM" FOR A REASON. IT HAPPENS SLOWLY, OVER TIME.

WHAT'S THE X-MEN'S TAKE ON THIS? THIS THING HAS ITS ROOTS IN THE MUTANT REGISTRATION ACT. SHOULDN'T WE PRESENT A UNITED FRONT, ONE WAY OR T'OTHER?

I DON'T KNOW WHAT'S UP WITH THE X-MEN LATELY. FOR INSTANCE, WHEN SCOTTY CAME BY THE OTHER DAY...

...HE SEEMED TO RECOGNIZE LAYLA. BUT THEN HE ACTED LIKE HE DIDN'T.

THAT'S IT? THAT'S ALL YOU'VE GOT FOR ACCUSATIONS?

MAYBE THAT'S ENOUGH. THAT KID... I DUNNO. COULD BE A SPY.

WHO'S A SPY?

YOU TELL ME.

NO ONE THAT I KNOW OF.

NICE ANSWER.

YOU KNOW WHAT'S FUNNY ABOUT ANSWERS?

FINDING THEM ISN'T *ALWAYS* THE BEST THING.

BRRIIIING BRRIIIING

HUNH. YOU USUALLY TELL US WHEN THE PHONE'S ABOUT TO RING. LOSING YOUR TOUCH, LAYLA?

YOU SHOULDN'T TAKE THAT.

X-FACTOR.

YEAH, JAMIE, WHAT'S UP?

HI, LOOK...I KNOW THIS MIGHT SOUND A LITTLE PARANOID...

I'M TELLING YOU, THEY'RE *LYING* TO YOU! ALL THE SO-CALLED HEROES! THEY'RE OUT TO *GET* YOU! THEY'RE JEALOUS!

...BUT I'M STARTING TO WONDER IF MAYBE WE'VE BEEN LOOKING IN THE WRONG DIRECTION ABOUT THE DECIMATION. HERE'S WHAT I'D LIKE YOU TO DO...

WHAT'D HE SAY?

HE WANTS ME TO START TALKING TO HIGH-PROFILE DO-GOODERS, TO FIND OUT IF THEY KNOW ANYTHING ABOUT M-DAY.

YOU MEAN SOMETHING THE X-MEN DON'T ALREADY KNOW ABOUT?

OR MAYBE SOMETHING THEY DO KNOW ABOUT AND HAVEN'T TOLD US.

LIKE WHAT?

LIKE I-DON'T-KNOW-WHAT. ANY THOUGHTS ON THAT, LAYLA?

YEAH. YOU HOLDING BACK ON US, LIKE YOU DID ABOUT SIRYN GETTING HURT?

WOULD YOU BELIEVE ME IF I TOLD YOU?

PROBABLY NOT, SO I GUESS THERE'S NO POINT.

OKEY-DOKEY.

WHY ARE YOU MAKING THIS MORE AND MORE DIFFICUL—?

I'M JUST A KID, FOR GOD'S SAKE.

HMM! THAT SHOWS A GREAT DEAL OF MUSCLE CONTROL, MONET.

NOT REALLY. ACTUALLY, I'M--

WAIT A MINUTE...? MADROX?

WHAT'S WITH THE NEW OUTFIT? WHAT'S--

IT'S A DUPE. YOU'RE ONE OF MADROX'S DUPLICATES, RIGHT?

I PREFER THE TERM "CO-ORIGINAL," ACTUALLY.

WHY DID JAMIE SEND BACK A DUPE? DID HE FORGET SOMETHING?

HE DIDN'T. I WORK FOR THE GOVERNMENT.

I'M HERE TO SIGN YOU UP PURSUANT TO THE SUPER HERO REGISTRATION ACT.

OH, ARE YOU NOW?

OOOOO. HE WORKS FOR "THE GOVERNMENT." A DUPE WALKS IN AND STARTS TOSSING AROUND ORDERS LIKE HE'S THE ACTUAL BOSS AROUND HERE.

WHO THE HELL DO YOU THINK YOU ARE?

ALLOW ME TO INTRODUCE MYSELF:

JAMIE MADROX: AGENT OF S.H.I.E.L.D.

IT'S A MIRACLE! A FREAKIN' MIRACLE!

HE DID IT! PIETRO DID IT! I CAN FLY AGAIN!

YOU...TALKED TO HIM?!? YOU LET HIM LAY HANDS ON YOU! YOU WEREN'T SUPPOSED TO DO THAT?!

WHAT'RE YOU YAMMERING ABOUT, BRAT?!

YOU AND YOUR FRIEND WERE SUPPOSED TO CHASE HIM AND THEN HE WAS GOING TO SHUNT INTO THE NEAR FUTURE TO GET AWAY, AND HE WAS GONNA WIND UP IN THE PATH OF A TRUCK AND WHAM! YOU MESSED THINGS UP, YOU...YOU BIG DUMMY!

LOOK, I DUNNO WHAT YOUR PROBLEM IS, BUT I'M COMING DOWN THERE TO TEACH YOU SOME MAN--

WHA--?! I... I CAN'T LAND! NO! NO!!!!

NNNOOOOOOOOO

I TRY TO DO THE RIGHT THING, AND IT TURNS OUT WRONG.

I KNOW THAT'S HOW IT IS FOR EVERYONE ELSE...BUT NOT FOR ME. IS THIS SOME KIND OF SICK JOKE?

YOU GOTTA BE *KIDDIN'* ME.

YOU'RE LUCKY ENOUGH TO COP SKIN SAMPLES FROM TRYP AND TRYP JUNIOR, AND YOU TRUST 'EM *TO THIS* DUMP? YOU SAID IT WAS A LAB!

IT IS.

IT LOOKS LIKE A BOMB HIT IT!

OH, SPEAKIN' OF HITTIN', SORRY I BUMPED *INTO* YA BEFORE, AND IT MADE--

A DUPE, YEAH. I REABSORBED HIM. NO BIG DEAL.

YOU WERE TALKIN' TO HIM A LOT B'FORE YOU DID. WHAT ABOUT?

NOTHING. NO BIG DEAL.

OH! MADDY! TOOK YOUR SWEET TIME GETTING HERE.

YOU'RE NOT THE ONLY GUY I DO JOBS FOR, Y'KNOW. I'M IN DEMAND.

YEAH, I'LL BET. 'CAUSE, Y'KNOW, THIS PLACE IS SO EFFICIENT.

YOU GOT A PROBLEM WITH THE WAY I RUN THINGS?

AW, C'MON. THIS PLACE IS LIKE SOMETHIN' OUT OF A 1950S B-MOVIE! WHO DO YOU THINK YOU ARE, CALLING IT "MODERN LABS?"

WELL, HE PROBABLY THINKS HE'S THE OWNER, DOCTOR MALCOLM MODERN.

JEEEEZ...

LOOK, BIG MAN, IF YOU DON'T WANT MY HELP, JUST SAY SO...

WE WANT YOUR HELP, DOC. GUIDO HERE JUST DOESN'T KNOW YOU'RE THE BEST IN THE BUSINESS.

WHAT BUSINESS WOULD THAT BE?

SHUT... UP.

FINE, WHATEVER. SORRY ABOUT DISSIN' YOUR... WHATEVER THIS IS.

"THIS" IS HOW I MAINTAIN CONFIDENTIALITY. IF I KEPT EVERYTHING NICE AND ORGANIZED, UNAUTHORIZED PEOPLE COULD COME IN AND FIND ANYTHING IN SECONDS.

MY WAY DISCOURAGES SPIES. NO SYSTEM. JUST PURE MEMORIZATION.

SOMETIMES DOING STUFF "WRONG" HIDES THAT YOU'RE DOING SOMETHING RIGHT.

HERE WE GO.

THE FOLDER'S MARKED "WEIRD."

THAT'S 'CAUSE WHAT I FOUND WAS WEIRD. THIS SAMPLE YOU BROUGHT IN...IT'S LIKE NOTHING I'VE EVER SEEN.

MEANING WHAT?

MEANING IF THERE'S ANYTHING LIKE IT, I HAVEN'T SEEN IT. THERE'S SOME TOTALLY NEW DNA MARKERS IN HERE. COMPLETELY UNCHARTED.

YOU'RE SAYING HE'S... WHAT? ALIEN?

HE'S PART OF THE HUMAN RACE, IF THAT'S WHAT YOU MEAN. HE'S A SUBSPECIES, SAME AS MUTANTS. BUT A DIFFERENT SUB-SPECIES.

I THOUGHT MUTANTS AND HUMANS WERE DIFFERENT RACES.

NEVER COTTONED TO THAT THINKING. HISTORY'S FILLED WITH TOO MANY CASES OF ONE TYPE OF HUMAN DECIDING ANOTHER TYPE WEREN'T HUMAN, USUALLY FOLLOWED BY HILARITY AND DEATH.

ANYWAY... WHATEVER THIS GUY IS...HE AIN'T LIKE YOU OR ME OR ANYTHING ELSE.

OKAY... THAT'S TRYP. WHAT ABOUT THE OTHER GUY?

WHAT OTHER GUY?

HIS SON. JUNIOR.

MADDY, I DUNNO WHAT THE HELL YOU'RE TALKIN' ABOUT.

THE TWO SAMPLES YOU GAVE ME...I JUST FIGURED YOU WERE PLAYING IT SAFE.

SAFE? I DON'T--?

THE TWO SAMPLES ARE EXACT DNA MATCHES. THEY'RE THE SAME GUY.

PUT IT DOWN. YOU'RE NOT GETTING AWAY...

YOU'RE THE ONE NOT GETTING AWAY! MAN, I CAN'T *WAIT* UNTIL ALL YOU JERKS HAVE T'COME CLEAN WITH YOUR I.D.S! THAT'LL BE *SWEET!*

YOU BETTER BE LIVIN' IN FREAKIN' FORT KNOX, MAN! 'CAUSE ONCE GUYS LIKE ME FIND OUT WHO YOU ARE, GUYS LIKE YOU'LL BE--

AHHHH!!

MY HAND! MY FREAKING *HAND* IS BROKE!

KRAK

MATCHES YOUR *JAW.*

UNFFFFFF!!!

NICE WORK, SPIDER-MAN.

SAME TO YOU. GOOD AIM, SMASHING HIS GUN APART WITH THAT...WHATTAYA CALL IT?

SONIC LANCE. *NOT* SO GOOD AIM, ACTUALLY. I WAS GOING FOR HIS HEAD.

OH.

WELL... GOOD JOB EITHER WAY. I HEARD WHAT HE WAS SAYING ABOUT THE REG ACT. JUST ANOTHER REASON WHY IT'S A BAD IDEA.

I DUNNO ABOUT THAT. HUNDREDS OF PEOPLE DIED BECAUSE OF THE NEW WARRIORS. WHATEVER HAPPENED TO TAKING RESPONSIBILITY?

WHAT, DID THEY GET TO YOU, TOO?

NOBODY *"GOT"* TO ME.

OH NO? A GUY CLIMBED OVER A CIRCUS FENCE AND REACHED INTO A CAGE TO PET THE TIGER. THE ANIMAL RIPPED HIS ARM OFF.

HE SUED THE CIRCUS, SAYING THEY SHOULD'VE HAD TALLER FENCES. HE WON.

LOOK, I'M NOT SAYING THAT--

A BURGLAR WAS CLIMBING AROUND ON A ROOF, TRYING TO REACH A SKYLIGHT TO BREAK IN. THE ROOF COLLAPSED. HE SUED THE HOME OWNER AND WON.

THE NEW WARRIORS WEREN'T RESPONSIBLE FOR ALL THOSE DEATHS! THE BAD GUYS THEY TOOK DOWN WERE!

BUT SINCE THE BAD GUYS CAN'T BEAT US IN THE FIELD, THEY'RE TRYING TO BEAT US THROUGH THE COURTS AND, NOW, THROUGH CONGRESS...

...IN A WORLD THAT CAN'T DISTINGUISH BETWEEN WHO'S ON THE SIDE OF THE ANGELS AND WHO'S PLAYING FOR SATAN. AND YOU'RE OKAY WITH THAT?

OBVIOUSLY NOT!

BUT ARE YOU OKAY WITH THE PUBLIC NOT BEING ABLE TO DISTINGUISH? BECAUSE I'M NOT. THEY HAVE TO KNOW WE'RE ON THEIR SIDE, AND MAYBE THE ONLY WAY TO LET THEM KNOW IS TO BE HONEST.

YOU BELIEVE IN HONESTY THAT MUCH?

SURE.

THEN WHY NOT BE A SWEET-HEART...AAAND TELLLLL ME EVVVVVERYTHING YOU KNOW ABOUT THE DECIMAAATION...? PLEEEEEASE?

SUUURE. YOU BET.

HEY, RAHNE.

HEY YUIRSELF. WHAT'RE YE DOING OUT HERE, LAYLA?

WAITING.

FOR WHAT?

I'LL KNOW WHEN IT GETS HERE.

OOOKAY.

YOURRR... FAULT...

...ALL...YOUR... FAULT...HE DID THIS...TOOOO MEEE...

...CAAAAAUUUUSE OF YOOOO...

AND SIGN HERE...AND INITIAL HERE... EXCELLENT.

JAMIE?!? WHAT'S GOING ON--?

HELLO, RAHNE. IT'S BEEN, SUBJECTIVELY SPEAKING, AGES.

HE'S FROM S.H.I.E.L.D. DON'T ASK.

HOW CAN HE BE FROM S.H.I.E.L.D.? AH DON'T...?

I TELL HER "DON'T ASK" AND SHE ASKS. IF YOU DON'T SPEAK WITH A COMIC-OPERA BROGUE, SHE DOESN'T UNDERSTAND A WORD YOU SAY.

JAMIE DISPATCHED ME SOME TIME AGO TO STUDY ESPIONAGE. VAL COOPER WOUND UP PUTTING ME TOGETHER WITH S.H.I.E.L.D.

YOUR ASSOCIATES ARE DOING THEIR CIVIC DUTY AND COMPLYING WITH THE SUPER HERO REGISTRATION ACT.

YE DON'T HAVE PROBLEMS WITH THIS IDEA?

WHY SHOULD WE? RICTOR'S POWERLESS ANYWAY, AND I'VE NOTHING TO HIDE.

THAT'S TRUE. I SAW IT ALL, AND SHE HAD NOTHING THERE WORTH HIDING.

COLLISION COURSE

X-FACTOR
A MARVEL COMICS EVENT

CIVIL
WAR

TRUST ISSUES

YOU'D DO IT AGAIN?!? KNOWING WHAT YOU COST US, YOU HAVE THE GALL TO SAY THAT YOU'D DO IT ALL OVER AGAIN!?!?

EASY, RICTOR...

YOU TAKE IT EASY, RAHNE! YOU'VE GOT POWERS! ALL I'VE GOT IS MEMORY! AND IT'S ALL THANKS TO THIS SMUG, UNAPOLOGETIC--!

I'M SORRY FOR YOUR PAIN, IF THAT MEANS ANYTHING.

IT MEANS JACK!

SO MUCH FOR THE SIN OF BEING UNAPOLOGETIC.

BUT MY SISTER'S LIFE MEANS EVERY-THING TO ME.

AND THEY WERE GOING TO KILL HER. IRON MAN AND THESE OTHERS...

...THE ONES WHO NOW COOPERATE WITH THE GOVERNMENT'S OPPRESSIVE ACTIONS...

...THEY WERE GOING TO PUT HER DOWN LIKE A RABID DOG.

YEAH? MEBBE THAT WOULDN'TA BEEN SUCH A BAD IDEA!

AND MEBBE WE SHOULD DO THAT TO YOU.

SCREWIN' UP THE LIVES OF MILLIONS FOR THE SAKE OF ONE PERSON?

I DIDN'T KNOW THAT WOULD BE THE OUTCOME.

BUT YOU SHOULD'VE!

ALL RIGHT. HERE, THEN, IS WHAT YOU SHOULD KNOW...

THANKS TO THE TERRIGEN MISTS OF THE INHUMANS...I'M ABLE TO RESTORE MUTANTS' POWERS WITH MY TOUCH ALONE.

HOWEVER, I DON'T KNOW WHAT WOULD HAPPEN IF I USED THAT TOUCH ON SOMEONE WHO STILL *HAS* POWERS... SUCH AS YOU.

PERHAPS NOTHING.

OR PERHAPS YOU MIGHT EXPLODE INTO A MILLION PIECES.

I WOULD *HATE* TO HAVE TO FIND OUT.

VERY WISE.

ESPECIALLY SINCE WE NEED TO BE UNITED AGAINST THE COMMON ENEMY.

I THINK IF WE POLL THE POPULATION OF MUTANT TOWN, THEY'LL BE AGREED THAT THE COMMON ENEMY IS YOU, YOU POMPOUS CLOWN.

I *LIKE* YOU, MONET ST. CROIX. YOU REMIND ME OF *ME* WHEN I WAS YOUNG. FULL OF PISS AND VINEGAR. BUT THEN...

YOU TOOK A SHOWER?

I GREW UP, AND REALIZED THE WORLD IS FILLED WITH HARD CHOICES. I'VE MADE MINE. YOU'RE GOING TO HAVE TO MAKE YOURS.

I DON'T DISPUTE THE PAIN I'VE CAUSED. BUT I'M HERE TO MAKE THINGS BETTER.

MEANWHILE THE GOVERNMENT HAS RETOOLED THE MUTANT REGISTRATION ACT...AND THIS TIME, IT'S TAKEN ROOT.

TODAY, REGISTRATION. TOMORROW, CAMPS. THE ENEMY YOU KNOW VERSUS THE ENEMY YOU DON'T. PICK YOUR POISON.

OH GOD...

JAMIE...

HERE IT COMES.

...WHAT DO *YOU* THINK?

YEAH. WHAT'S YOUR TAKE ON THIS?

WHOSE SIDE IS X-FACTOR ON, ANYWAY?

DO WE TELL EVERYONE WHAT HAPPENED?

SHOULD WE LET FAST-FEET SET UP SHOP HERE?

AS IF YOU COULD STOP ME.

SHOULD WE *TRY* TO STOP HIM?

WHAT ABOUT THE REG ACT? WHAT ABOUT THAT?

SO, MADROX, WHAT'S--?

214

X-FACTOR DETECTIVE AGENCY

214

YEAH, *THAT* HELPED.

X-FACTOR DETECTIVE AGENCY

YOU REALLY *AREN'T* ANY GOOD AT MAKING DECISIONS, *ARE* YOU?

THAT'S WHAT YOU NEED *ME* FOR. TO TELL YOU WHAT TO DO. OR AT LEAST POINT YOU IN THE RIGHT DIRECTION.

YEAH? AND WHAT DIRECTION SHOULD I GO IN NOW?

NORTH. NEAR THE INTERSECTION OF BUCHANAN AND BROADWAY.

IT'LL HELP YOU MAKE UP YOUR MIND ABOUT THE REGISTRATION ACT, IF THAT'S OF ANY USE. OH, AND BUY A HAT ON THE WAY. A WATCH CAP, PREFERABLY. AND A SCARF AND GLOVES.

FINE. BUT JUST SO YOU KNOW, THIS ISN'T *OVER* BETWEEN US.

YEAH? WHAT MAKES YOU SAY THAT?

THAT'S TRUE. WE'LL BE ARGUING FOR *A LONG* TIME TO COME.

'CAUSE EVENTUALLY WE GET MARRIED.

SHEESH.

AEGIS! COME OUT SLOWLY AND MAKE NO SUDDEN MOVES.

WE HAVE WEAPONS THAT CAN PUNCH THROUGH EVEN YOUR FORCE FIELD, SON. BUT YOU WON'T BE INJURED IF YOU SURRENDER IMMEDIATELY!

COMPLY WITH THE LAW, OR WE WILL BE FORCED TO--

DO YOU HEAR SOMETHING? LIKE... THE GROUND RUMBLING?

SOUNDS LIKE...A STAMPEDE.

GIVE ME A VIDEO REPORT FROM THE 'BOT!

SCANNING NOW, SIR.

WHAT THE HECK IS GOING ON IN THERE? I THOUGHT ONLY TWO PEOPLE WENT IN THERE...OUR SUBJECT AND SOME BYSTANDER.

YES, SIR. BUT IT'S...MUCH MORE CROWDED NOW. I GOT A READING ON--

WHA--?

YOU'RE OUT OF YOUR MIND! YOU GOTTA BE!

I HEAR THAT A LOT. I THINK WE'RE IN THE CLEAR.

IF YOU WANT, I CAN BRING YOU BACK TO X-FACTOR HEAD-QUARTERS...

THAT'S AN AMAZINGLY *LOUSY* IDEA. YOU DON'T WANT TO GET ANY DEEPER INTO THIS THAN YOU ARE.

THERE'S STEAM TUNNELS AND SUCH ACCESSIBLE THROUGH THE SUBWAYS. WITH ANY LUCK, I'LL FIND CAPTAIN AMERICA.

THANKS. I OWE YOU.

YOU DON'T OWE ME A THING.

OKAY, GOOD, 'CAUSE I'M NOT REALLY SURE HOW I'D REPAY YOU, SO...

LATER.

HE WAS JUST TRYING TO HELP PEOPLE, AND THEY'RE TREATING HIM LIKE HE'S A TERRORIST OR WORSE.

IT'S LIKE BEING TRAPPED AT THE MAD TEA PARTY.

OKAY, FIRST THINGS FIRST. TIME TO CALL ALLY-ALLY-OUT-ARE-IN-FREE.

YES. YES, THIS SHOULD WORK NICELY.

I'M PLEASED TO HEAR THAT, MR. MAXIMUS.

MAXIMOFF. MAXIMUS IS AN INHUMAN MADMAN WITH DELUSIONS OF POWER.

UHM...ALL RIGHT. MY MISTAKE. I'M SURE NO ONE WOULD THINK SUCH A THING OF YOU.

YOU HAVE NO IDEA.

QUICKSILVER!

CASE IN POINT.

IS...IS THAT...? THEM?

YES.

I'M AFRAID SO. I SUGGEST YOU LEAVE IMMEDIATELY. THEY CAN BECOME... VIOLENT...WHEN PROVOKED.

ARE...ARE YOU GOING TO PROVOKE THEM?

NO. BUT THEY'LL LIKELY BECOME VIOLENT ANYWAY.

SCANDALOUS, REALLY, HOW THEY CARRY ON.

QUICKSILVER! WE KNOW YOU'RE IN THERE!

WE CAN *SMELL* YA FROM A MILE OFF, FOR STARTERS.

WELL... *SOME* OF US CAN.

I SUGGEST YOU SURRENDER IMMEDIATELY!

YOU "*SUGGEST*" IT? TRULY?

VERY WELL. LET ME CONSIDER IT. *HMMM.*

NO.

A NICE LADY IS ABOUT TO EMERGE. KINDLY LET HER DEPART UNHARMED.

DON'T HURT ME! I... I DON'T HAVE POWERS!

SHE *IS* AWARE THAT WE ARE THE GOOD GUYS, CORRECT?

THESE DAYS, HANK, I THINK PEOPLE WOULDN'T KNOW THE GOOD GUYS IF THEY CAME UP AND *BIT* THEM.

AN *INTERESTING* HYPOTHESIS. SHALL I PUT IT TO THE TEST...?

THEY KNOW.

WHA--?

THEY KNOW. X-FACTOR KNOWS YOU LIED TO THEM ABOUT THE DECIMATION.

I DIDN'T TELL THEM. THEY FOUND OUT THEMSELVES.

I WISH THEY *HADN'T*, BUT...THERE IT IS.

I DON'T KNOW WHAT YOU'RE DOING HERE, LAYLA... BUT YOU SHOULD RUN HOME TO YOUR FOLKS...

I DON'T HAVE ANY FOLKS.

WHAT? BUT...YOU SAID...

I LIED. IN THE... "OTHER" WORLD... I HAD PARENTS. BUT NOT BEFORE. AND NOT NOW.

I HAD THIS NICE DREAM OF THEM, JUST BEFORE THINGS CHANGED BACK. MY MOM WAS CALLING ME, TELLING ME IT WAS TIME FOR SCHOOL.

THEN I WOKE UP, BACK IN THE ORPHANAGE.

BACK IN THE WORLD I HATED.

WHY DID YOU LIE?

NO, YOU DIDN'T.

I HAD TO.

YES, I DID. BUT NOW THE LIES ARE FALLING APART...AND X-FACTOR...

...IS HERE.

AND IT'S SOOO NICE OF YOU TO BE SHOWING US THE RESPECT WE DESERVE, SCOTT, BY TELLING US THAT YOU'D BE COMING INTO MUTANT TOWN AFTER PIETRO.

WAIT. YOU DIDN'T CALL.

MAYBE WE SHOULD BE, OH, WAITING BY THE PHONE? IS *THAT* WHERE YOU'LL BE WANTING US, THEN? LIKE A DATELESS COLLEEN ON FRIDAY NIGHT?

THERESA...NOW ISN'T THE BEST TIME TO DISCUSS THIS.

WE RECEIVED A TIP THAT QUICKSILVER IS--

WE KNOW. I PHONED IT IN.

WE FIGURED IT WAS THE BEST WAY TO GET YOU OUT HERE SO WE CAN...CHAT.

YOU WANNA THROW DOWN WITH US? TO PROTECT THAT SILVER-HEADED SLIMEBALL?

HE MAY BE A SLIMEBALL. HE MAY BE A TOTALLY EVIL MONSTER.

YOU KNOW I CAN *HEAR* YOU, RIGHT?

BUT HE DIDN'T PRETEND TO BE OUR FRIEND, AND HE DIDN'T LIE TO US. CAN *YOU* SAY THE SAME?

THIS IS *RIDICULOUS.* WE DON'T HAVE TO DEFEND OUR ACTIONS. WE DID WHAT HAD TO BE DONE.

AND WE'RE GOING TO DO THAT NOW AS WELL. STAND ASIDE--

COLOSSUS, WAIT--!

SCREEEEEEEE

OOOOOFFF!!

DON'T YOU SEE? THIS IS WHAT QUICKSILVER WANTS! TO TURN US AGAINST EACH OTHER!

BUT IF YOU CAN'T SEE THAT FOR YOUR-SELVES...

...THEN WE'LL DRIVE THE POINT HOME!

THIS IS GONNA HURT...BUT IT'LL BE WORTH IT.

IT TOOK DOZENS OF FOOT-STOMPINGS AND WALL-POUNDINGS TO PRODUCE AS MANY DUPES AS I DID IN THE ALLEY.

THE CONCUSSIVE FORCE OF CYCLOPS' BLAST, ON THE OTHER HAND...

Hotel

...CUTS RIGHT TO THE CHASE.

THAT ALL YOU GOT, SCOTTY? HUH? WANT TO TAKE *ANOTHER* SHOT?

MAKE FIFTY MORE OF ME? MAYBE A HUNDRED?

C'MON, SCOTTY! *BRING* IT! *EMPOWER* ME! MAKE ENOUGH OF ME TO KICK YOUR ASTONISHING X-BUTTS AROUND THE BLOCK ALL BY MYSELF, WITH THE REST OF MY CREW ALONG TO PICK UP THE PIECES!

C'MON!

C'MON!!!

YOU WANT PIECES, KID? THAT CAN BE ARRANGED.

BACK OFF, LOGAN.

I *TRUSTED* YOU, MAN!!!

EVERY-BODY LIES. GET OVER IT.

WE *COULDN'T* LET PEOPLE KNOW THE TRUTH. IT WOULD'VE CAUSED A WORLDWIDE PANIC.

IF EVERYONE KNEW THAT A SINGLE MUTANT COULD RECREATE THE WORLD IN HER OWN IMAGE...OBLITERATE POWERS WITH A FEW WORDS...

HUMANS WOULD HAVE WANTED TO DESTROY ANY REMAINING MUTANTS...

THEY'VE WANTED T'DESTROY US FOR YEARS, SCOTTY. THAT'S NOTHING NEW.

WHAT'S *NEW* IS THAT YE DIDN'T TRUST US WITH THE *TRUTH*.

YE'RE SO INTERESTED IN PROTECTING PEOPLE? WHAT ABOUT THE REGISTRATION ACT? PIETRO SAYS THE GOVERNMENT'S FAR MORE DANGEROUS THAN HE COULD EVER BE.

WHERE DO YE STAND ON THAT?

CONSIDERING ALL YOUR TIME WITH US, RAHNE, I'D THINK YOU WOULD APPRECIATE THE IMPORTANCE OF TRAINING...AND THE DANGERS OF USING POWERS WITHOUT IT.

"WHEN THEY CAME FOR ME, THERE WAS NO ONE LEFT TO SPEAK OUT."

EMMA ALREADY DISCUSSED IT WITH STARK. OFFICIALLY, WE'RE NEUTRAL. WE HAVE ENOUGH ISSUES OF OUR OWN TO DEAL WITH. BESIDES...

...WHAT SPARKED IT WAS UNTRAINED HEROES. LOOSE CANNONS.

WHA--? WHERE DID--?

THE WORDS OF MARTIN NIEMOLLER, EXPLAINING WHY DOING NOTHING ENCOURAGES MONSTERS SUCH AS HITLER, AND HIS ATROCITIES. WHERE IS THE VIGILANCE ONE WOULD EXPECT FROM THE X-MEN?

WE DON'T NEED TO BE LECTURED BY YOU, PIETRO.

AND THE U.S. GOVERNMENT, AND ITS REPRESENTATIVES, AREN'T HITLER AND HIS POWER-GRABBING NAZIS.

AS I RECALL...HITLER DIDN'T GRAB POWER. HE WAS ELECTED.

OKAY, HE'S GONE AGAIN! IS ANYBODY ELSE GETTING WEIRDED-OUT BY THIS?

I'M CALLING A PRESS CONFERENCE, SCOTT. I'M ANNOUNCING THAT X-FACTOR IS OPPOSED TO THE SUPERHUMAN REGISTRATION ACT.

I'M GOING TO SAY WE THINK IT'S WRONG. AND THAT IF ANYONE WANTS OUR AID IN AVOIDING THE GOVERNMENT, THEY JUST NEED TO ASK.

YOU'VE BEEN LYING TO US EVER SINCE THE DECIMATION. ARE YOU GOING TO HAVE OUR BACKS FOR THIS?

WE CAN'T. WE'VE ALREADY AGREED TO--

THEN GET THE HELL OUT OF MUTANT TOWN, OR IT'S GOING TO BE "GOOD GUY" MUTANT VERSUS "GOOD GUY" MUTANT, AND WE'LL HAVE OUR OWN LITTLE CIVIL WAR RIGHT HERE.

OKAY, THAT'S IT. I'M--

LET'S GO.

WHAT?

SCOTT, WE CAN--

I KNOW WHAT WE CAN DO. AND I SAID WE'RE GOING.

WE'LL BE MONITORING QUICKSILVER, MADROX. IF HE SETS FOOT OUTSIDE OF MUTANT TOWN, WE'RE ALL OVER HIM. OTHERWISE, HE'S YOUR PROBLEM NOW, 24/7.

ENJOY YOUR LITTLE KINGDOM HERE. AND GOD HELP YOU WHEN IT ALL COMES CRASHING DOWN...

...BECAUSE WE WON'T.

MADROX... DID WE JUST WIN?

GOD AS MY WITNESS, RAHNE...I HAVEN'T THE FAINTEST IDEA.

CABLE & DEADPOOL

A MARVEL COMICS EVENT

CIVIL WAR

"ONCE, A TRAGIC DIVIDE ROCKED THE STARS AND STRIPES. CIVIL STRIFE PITCHED BROTHER AGAINST BROTHER. BLUE VERSUS GREY.

"IT WAS A TERRIBLE TIME, BLOOD AND GUTS AND EVERYTHING IN VERY DEPRESSING *SEPIA*.

"IT WAS CALLED THE *WAR BETWEEN THE STATES*, BUT NOW WE CALL IT THE CIVIL WAR, LIKE WE OWN THE TITLE OR SOMETHING...

"... AND NOW MARVEL HAS THEIR VERY OWN *CIVIL WAR*™--DO WE HAVE A ™? WE ARE TALKING ABOUT TRADEMARK LAWYERS WHO ONCE TRIED TO PUT A ™ ON THE WORD *DEATH*™, SO...

"IT STARTED WITH THOSE LOSER *NEW WARRIORS*® DWEEBS SCREWING UP AND MAKING A BAD GUY CALLED *NITRO*™ BLOW UP AND TAKE A SCHOOL IN *STAMFORD* OUT WITH HIM.

"SPEAKING OF WHICH, ALL THAT LED TO A NATIONAL *SUPERHUMAN REGISTRATION ACT*. ALL MASKS HAVE TO SIGN UP AND BE GOOD GOVERNMENT BOY SCOUTS.

"AND LEADING THE CHARGE, IN QUITE A SURPRISE REVEAL THAT COULD SCREW UP HIS CONTINUITY FOR YEARS TO COME, WAS *SPIDER-MAN*..."

...WHO TOOK HIS MASK OFF ON *NATIONAL TV* AND, LIKE, *TOTALLY* GOT ME OFF THE HOOK FOR THROWING HIM OUT OF A MOVING CAR ON THE *QUEENS-BOROUGH BRIDGE!*

ANYWAY, NOW THERE'RE HEROES WHO ARE REGISTERING AND A WHOLE BUNCH WHO *AREN'T*.

THE ONES WHO *DID* DON'T HAVE TIME TO TRACK DOWN THE ONES WHO *DIDN'T* ON ACCOUNT OF VILLAINS TAKING ADVANTAGE OF THE BIG CLUSTER&^%$.

AND THAT'S WHERE I COME IN...

THE HERO HUNTER
A MARVEL CIVIL WAR TIE-IN

AND WHY ARE YOU TELLING ME ALL THIS?

BECAUSE I WANTED YOU TO KNOW WHAT YOU ARE UP AGAINST.

AND RENEW THE OFFER I MADE TO YOU BEFORE I CAME HERE.

CABLE... THANK YOU, BUT WE'RE NOT LEAVING THE COUNTRY.

ASYLUM IN PROVIDENCE--A BREAK FROM ALL THIS ON A BEAUTIFUL SOUTH PACIFIC ISLAND SOUNDS... APPEALING--

--BUT LEAVING NOW WOULD SEND A VERY WRONG MESSAGE.

YOU...YOU'RE STILL THINKING LIKE CAPTAIN AMERICA...I THOUGHT AFTER YOUR VISIT TO PROVIDENCE, AFTER OUR TALK...

I KNOW THE NEW SECRET IDENTITIES OF ALL YOUR RENEGADE HEROES!

IF I FOUND THEM WITHIN SECONDS OF YOUR FORGERIES BEING ELECTRONICALLY TRANSFERRED, HOW LONG BEFORE THEY UNCOVER THEM?

THEY DON'T HAVE ACCESS TO THE SAME LEVEL OF...ELECTRONIC TELEPATHY...THAT YOU DO NOW.

HERCULES: VICTOR TEGLER

GOLIATH: ROCKWELL DOBBSWORTH

DAREDEVIL: COOPER PEYTON

CAPTAIN AMERICA: ONETT HENDRICK

IT'S ONLY A MATTER OF TIME. THEY KNEW MOST OF YOUR ORIGINAL IDENTITIES BEFORE THIS ACT CAME INTO BEING, THEY JUST NEVER TOLD YOU!

NOW, THEY HAVE THE TWO GREATEST REASONS TO PRY-- FEAR AND RIGHTEOUS SELF-AGGRANDIZE-MENT!

YOU'RE SAYING WE'RE GOING TO LOSE?

I'M SAYING YOU'VE *ALREADY* LOST!

YOU KNOW THIS BECAUSE YOU'RE FROM THE *FUTURE* AND KNOW EVERY-THING, RIGHT?

NO...I'M SAYING THIS BECAUSE I'VE SEEN WHAT THEY HAVE PLANNED.

I KNOW THIS GOES *BEYOND* SECRET IDENTITIES AND REGISTRATION.

THIS WILL GROW INTO THE USE OF SUPER-HUMANS AS AN ORGANIZED, TOTALITARIAN *MILITARY PATROL.*

I KNOW *IRON MAN.* TONY STARK WOULD *NEVER* AGREE TO SOMETHING LIKE THAT.

AND WE'RE BACK TO SQUARE ONE. YOU'RE THINKING IN TERMS OF *MONTHS* AND *YEARS,* I'M TALKING ABOUT *DECADES* AND *CENTURIES.*

NATHAN...I'VE THOUGHT ABOUT OUR TALK A LOT...YOU CAN'T FIGHT TIME, YOU CAN'T CHANGE THE BIG PICTURE IN A *DAILY* STRUGGLE...

NO, BUT THROUGHOUT THE COURSE OF HISTORY, THE ACTIONS AND DECISIONS OF INDIVIDUALS--OR THEIR *NON-ACTIONS*--HAVE AFFECTED THE "BIG PICTURE."

MY OFFER OF ASYLUM IS IN CONSIDERATION OF THE BIG PICTURE-- THE *WORLD* PICTURE.

I AM PRESIDENT PRO TEM OF *RUMEKISTAN* NOW. EUROPEAN AND FORMER SOVIET BLOC COUNTRIES HAVE ALWAYS CONSIDERED SUPER-HUMANS A DANGEROUSLY "AMERICAN THING."

AND YOU CAN HELP MAKE IT A "DANGEROUSLY GLOBAL THING"--?

CYNICAL HUMOR DOESN'T WORK FOR YOU. GIVE UP THIS FIGHT TO WIN A MUCH, MUCH *BIGGER* ONE. THE FIGHT FOR THE *FUTURE!*

I CAN'T DO THAT.

CABLE & DEADPOOL
A MARVEL COMICS EVENT

CIVIL WAR

"HALF OF *STAMFORD* BLEW UP. NOT SO'S ANYONE WOULD NORMALLY CARE, EXCEPT IT HAPPENED NEAR A *SCHOOLYARD.*

"YOU KNOW HOW *EVERYTHING* GETS BLOWN OUT OF PROPORTION WHEN AMERICAN KIDS ARE BLOWN UP, RIGHT?

"SINCE IT WAS *SPANDEX HIJINKS* THAT CAUSED THE EXPLOSION, WHITE MEN IN SUITS DID WHAT THEY DO BEST--THEY PASSED *LAWS*--ALL SUPERHUMANS HAD TO *REGISTER* THEIR IDENTITIES.

"A BUNCHA HEROES SAID OKEY-DOKEY, A BUNCH SAID NO WAY.

"THE BOY SCOUT BRANCH MADE A BIG SHOW OF COOPERATING... BY HAVING *SPIDER-MAN* REVEAL HIS IDENTITY ON NATIONAL TV.

"AS IF WE *HADN'T* SEEN THE MOVIES ALREADY AND *DIDN'T* KNOW IT WAS DREAMY DOE-EYED *TOBEY MAGUIRE* UNDER THAT MASK!

"SO ANYWAY, WITH THE LINES DRAWN, *WHOSE SIDE ARE YOU ON?*

"GOOD OL' *WADE WILSON*, MERC WITH A MOUTH KNOWN FROM EARTH TO URANUS AS *DEADPOOL*, GOES FOR THE SIDE THAT *PAYS ME* TO KICK TUSHY.

"AND SINCE THE GOOD OL' U.S.OF A. DIVISION OF HOMELAND SECURITY SPENDS MONEY LIKE *CHARLES BARKLEY* ON A DRUNKEN BINGE IN *LAS VEGAS*...

"...I STARTED WORKING AS A *SUPERHUMAN BOUNTY HUNTER.* I GOT A *BADGE* AND EVERYTHING!

"MY OL' PAL, *NATHAN-DAYSPRING-ASKANI'SON*-ALSO-KNOWN-AS-*CABLE*-SOLDIER-FROM-THE-FUTURE-AND-WANNA-BE-WORLD-SAVIOR WAS MEETING WITH THE *OTHER SIDE*...

"... NAMELY THE LEADER OF THE RENEGADE HEROES, *CAPTAIN AMERICA.*

"SO WHILE THEY DID ALL KINDS OF PHILOSOPHICAL WINDBAGGING, I TRACKED THE SECRET HEROES BACK TO THEIR INCREDIBLY NOT-SO-SECRET HQ AND...

CASUALTIES OF WAR
A MARVEL CIVIL WAR TIE-IN

FINALLY!

I REALLY HAVE TO PEE.

THIS ISN'T A GAME ANY-MORE, *WADE*.

I WENT TO HELP THEM ON A MISSION. ONE OF OUR MEMBERS WAS *KILLED*.

WAIT A MINUTE-- *SERIOUS*--NOT BY ONE OF US *GOOD GUYS*--

--I GOT LIKE A SIX-HOUR LECTURE ON NOT CAPPING ANYONE!

SOMEONE FORGOT TO TELL THAT TO *THOR*.

THOR IS DEAD.

SOMEONE FORGOT TO TELL HIM THAT, TOO.

THAT KINDA SUCKS. I MEAN, WHICH ONE WAS IT? NOT THAT NUBILE *WICCAN* GUY, I HOPE.

I MEAN, LOSING ANY OF THOSE ADORABLE, TOP-SELLING *YOUNG AVENGERS* WOULD BE WRONG IN SO MANY WAYS...

JUST STOP...

I REALLY HAVE TO PEE.

WHAT'RE YOU DOING?

WHY'RE YOU TURNING OFF YOUR *GRAVIMETRIC FIELD* THINGIE?

BODYSLIDE BY TWO.

AAAH

NNFF

GAAAHH

YOU-- WHAT--ARE THEY--?

I CAN ACCESS AND MANIPULATE SOMETHING CALLED THE *INFONET*.

IT'S THE COMBINED TOTALITY OF THE PLANET'S *ELECTRONIC TRANSMISSIONS*.

THESE BOYS ARE HAVING THE CONTENTS OF THE *LIBRARY OF CONGRESS* DOWNLOADED INTO THEIR BRAINS.

IT'S NOT HURTING THEM. IT'LL *OVER- WHELM* THEM FOR AN HOUR OR SO.

SO YOU CAN DO WHAT, *ASSASSINATE* ME?

I THOUGHT YOUR *POLL NUMBERS* HAD ACCOMPLISHED THAT TASK.

I ONLY CAME TO TALK--CONVINCE YOU TO STOP THIS MADNESS...BUT I SEE NOW...

...THAT ONE MAN'S *MADNESS* IS ANOTHER MAN'S *RATIONAL* COURSE OF ACTION.

GUESS ONLY TIME WILL TELL, HUH?

HISTORY WILL NOT BE KIND TO YOU.

CASE YOU HADN'T NOTICED, THE *PRESENT* HASN'T BEEN ALL PRETZELS AND BEEF JERKY, EITHER.

THE NEXT TIME WE MEET, YOU'LL BE AN OLD, ENFEEBLED MAN...AND YOU'LL BE WATCHING YOUR SUCCESSOR SIX TIMES REMOVED...

...AS HE SIGNS A TREATY OF *SURRENDER.*

MAN, THOSE BATHROOMS MUST HAVE REALLY GOOD INSULATION!

YOU'RE A LEGALLY DEPUTIZED AGENT OF THE COMMISSION ON SUPER-HUMAN ACTIVITIES, RIGHT?

YES, SIR, MR. PRESIDENT! I GOT A BADGE. YOU WANT TO SEE IT?

NO, THAT'S OKAY, SON. WHAT I REALLY WANT YOU TO DO...

CABLE &
DEADPOOL
A MARVEL COMICS EVENT

CIVIL
WAR

"THE **NEW WARRIORS**, SUPER HEROES FOR THE DRAKE AND JOSH CROWD, JUMPED **NITRO** AND HE BLEW UP. HAPPENED NEAR A **SCHOOLYARD**. VERY MESSY.

"VERY WHITE MEN IN SUITS PASSED SOME LAWS. SPANDEXERS HAD TO REGISTER THEIR IDENTITIES WITH THE GOV.

"MOST HEROES DID; SOME SAID NO WAY, JOSE. I SAY, GO BACK TO MEXICO, YOU **CHIMICHANGAS!**

"THE GOVERNMENT, IN THEIR INFINITE WISDOM, HIRED ME TO BE ONE OF THEIR **RENEGADE SUPER HERO** HUNTERS. I GOT A **BADGE** AND EVERYTHING.

"ONLY IN AMERICA COULD I, **WADE WILSON**, THE MERC WITH A MOUTH KNOWN AS **DEADPOOL**, BE HIRED TO HUNT DOWN A GUY CALLED **CAPTAIN AMERICA**.

"SO ANYWAY, I WAS KICKIN' TOTAL 'NADS, BUT THEN I GOT BETRAYED BY MY FORMER BUDDY, NATHAN DAYSPRING ASKANI'SON CALIGULA, ALSO KNOWN AS **CABLE**.

"CABLE DID HIS **BODYSLIDE** THING AND TELEPORTED US TO THE **WHITE HOUSE**, WHICH HAS LOVELY LAVATORIES, BY THE WAY.

"VERY ELEGANT FAUCET FIXTURES. AND CUTE LITTLE SOAPS SHAPED LIKE MILLARD FILLMORE'S HEAD. HIGHLY RECOMMENDED.

"WHILE I WAS DOING MY BIZNESS, NATE MUST'VE GOTTEN **MORE** ARROGANT THAN USUAL, 'CAUSE WHEN I GOT BACK, I GOT MY ORDERS: TAKE CABLE DOWN-- **DEAD OR ALIVE!"**

A HOUSE DIVIDED
A MARVEL CIVIL WAR TIE-IN

FIRST THING I SAID WAS THAT I ONLY CAME TO **TALK**.

MY STAFF MUST'VE MISSED THE APPOINTMENT YOU MADE THROUGH PROPER DIPLOMATIC CHANNELS.

BUT SINCE THE GOVERNMENT DOESN'T RECOGNIZE MY PRESIDENCY IN RUMEKISTAN, WOULD THEY HAVE TAKEN MY CALL?

SEE, THAT'S THE TICKET, MR. PREZ-- KEEP NATE BUSY.

LONG AS HE'S BUSY TRYING TO CONVINCE YOU OF HOW **SMART** HE IS, THEN HE'S **NOT** SHOWING YOU HOW **TOUGH** HE IS.

MARINES'RE SCRAMBLED. WHITE HOUSE IS SURROUNDED. THERE IS NO WAY THIS ENDS WELL FOR YOU.

DEPENDS ON YOUR DEFINITION OF "WELL."

THEY CAN'T GET THROUGH THE GRAVITY SHIELD CABLE SET UP.

OKAY, NATE, GUESS YOU WIN--IF YOU CALL A COMPLETE STALEMATED WASTE OF TIME A VICTORY...

...BUT WHAT THE HECK HAVE YOU "**WON**"--?

NATE'S JAW UNCLENCHES JUST A BIT. NOW LET'S SEE IF THAT'S A GOOD THING OR NOT...

MR. PRESIDENT... I DIDN'T COME HERE TO WIN ANYTHING... OR FIGHT.

I JUST WANTED TO TELL YOU--FROM THE PERSPECTIVE OF SOMEONE WHO HAS SEEN *COUNTLESS* HISTORIES PASS BY LIKE THE PAGES OF A BOOK--

--THAT IN THE SHORT RUN, THIS MIGHT CREATE SOME SENSE OF *SECURITY* FROM SUPERHUMAN OR TERRORIST THREATS...

...BUT IN THE LONG RUN...THE PATH BEING TAKEN WILL PROVE TO BE A MISTAKE.

YOU THINK I DON'T AGONIZE OVER THAT? EVERYONE IN THIS ADMINISTRATION DOES. IN THE SHORT OR LONG HAUL--

--THE PEOPLE NEED TO BE *PROTECTED* FROM ANYTHING THAT THREATENS THEM AND THE COUNTRY.

WE DON'T HAVE THE ADVANTAGE--OR THE LUXURY--OF BEIN' FROM THE FUTURE AND ACTIN' LIKE WE KNOW WE'RE ALWAYS RIGHT.

OUR CONVERSATION GOT OFF ON THE WRONG FOOT.

IT DID. I GOT A BIT PEEVED. SAID SOME THINGS JUST TO PUSH YOUR BUTTONS. YOU HAVE A WAY OF RAISIN' HACKLES, YOU KNOW?

I'VE BEEN TOLD...

I HAVEN'T CHOSEN TO DO THIS BECAUSE I WAS ELECTED, SIR, OR BECAUSE I THINK I'M BETTER THAN ANYONE ELSE...

...I DO THIS BECAUSE SOMEONE *HAS* TO LEAD.

I WAS HOPING YOU MIGHT WANT TO *FOLLOW*...

AND THAT ANSWER RIGHT THERE *PROVES* TO ME THAT WE'RE DOIN' THE RIGHT THING.

WE REGULATE NUCLEAR WARHEADS, REGISTER GUNS...FOLKS WITH POWERS HAVE BECOME NO DIFFERENT THAN THAT.

REGISTRATION IS ONLY KEEPING AN *EYE* ON ME. BUT ONCE SOMEONE TELLS ME WHERE TO GO AND WHAT TO DO, THAT'S PUTTING A *GUN* TO MY HEAD.

THEN *REBELLION* BECOMES *SELF-DEFENSE.*

THINK ABOUT THAT, PLEASE, AND I'LL THINK MORE ABOUT WHAT YOU SAID.

HE TURNED OFF HIS FIELD! ONE SHOT--NOW--

BODYSLIDE BY TWO.

NERTZ.

PCHK PCHK PCHK PCHK PCHK PCHK PCHK PCHK PCHK

...NO, DON'T TICKLE ME THERE... YOU NAUGHTY, NAUGHTY...

UHM...

THE USUAL DREAM, HUH?

PRETTY MUCH.

I BROKE YOUR NOSE, HUH? THAT'S FUNNY.

EVIL, EVIL MAN!

HEY, HOW COME WE HAVE AN AUDIENCE?

I DUCT TAPED YOU AGAIN. THAT'S FUNNY, TOO.

SHOULD WE JUST WAIT UNTIL NATURE CALLS AGAIN?

HISTORY: The albino mutant known only as Caliban was recruited by Callisto, who used Caliban's mutant-tracking ability to assemble the underground mutant community later known as Morlocks. Caliban was named by Callisto after the grotesque being in William Shakespeare's play "The Tempest." Living in the sewers and abandoned subway tunnels beneath Manhattan's streets with the Morlocks, the naïve Caliban found a renewed sense of family, but still felt lonely among his fellow outcasts. One evening, Caliban sensed the presence of mutants in a New York City nightclub and entered to find the Dazzler (Alison Blaire) performing. Caliban's presence created panic, which X-Men members Storm and Kitty Pryde attempted to quell alongside Spider-Woman (Jessica Drew). During the chaos, Caliban kidnapped Pryde and fled. Intercepted by the heroes, Caliban explained that he only wanted a friend like himself. Invited to join the X-Men, Caliban chose instead to return to the Morlocks.

When Callisto abducted the X-Man Angel (Warren Worthington III) and brought the Morlocks into conflict with the X-Men, Pryde was infected by the Morlock named Plague and found by Caliban. Caring for her, Caliban realized he could not cure her and panicked over what to do. Pryde promised to remain with him forever if he helped her and the X-Men. Unsure of what to do, Caliban sought help from Callisto; however, Callisto refused to allow the X-Men to leave, and only after she was defeated by Storm in ritual combat were the X-Men free to go. Storm offered the Morlocks a home and sanctuary with the X-Men, but Caliban, speaking for the group, declined the offer. When Pryde failed to make good on her promise, Callisto ordered her capture and attempted to force her to marry Caliban; however, Caliban realized Pryde did not truly love him, and released her from her promise. When the sorcerer Kulan Gath warped reality in Manhattan, transforming it to resemble his native era (circa 10, 000 B.C.), Caliban was merged with the X-Men's founder Charles Xavier, and forced to serve as Kulan Gath's familiar.

Soon after, the Morlocks were attacked by the Marauders, who began slaughtering the community. Injured in the massacre, Caliban was saved by his fellow Morlock Leech, and the pair were rescued from the Marauders by Power Pack and X-Factor (Angel, Beast, Cyclops, Iceman & Marvel Girl). Caliban subsequently resided at X-Factor's headquarters, briefly leaving to accompany the surviving Morlocks back underground before returning to join X-Factor in opposing anti-mutant organization the Right. Desperate to avenge the slaughter of his people, Caliban became colder and harder during his brief stint with X-Factor. After a battle against the Horsemen of Apocalypse, Caliban became increasingly frustrated with his passive power's inability to grant him the revenge he sought. When X-Factor subsequently encountered Apocalypse, Caliban swore to serve him as his Hellhound in exchange for power enough to exact revenge. Apocalypse genetically altered Caliban to increase his size and strength. After Caliban proved his worth against the likes of Archangel, Sabretooth and Cable's New Mutants, Apocalypse granted Caliban a place in his Horsemen as Death. With the Horsemen, Caliban fought the X-Men but was defeated, unaware that the Apocalypse he and his fellow Horsemen were serving at the time proved to be Mister Sinister in disguise.

Separated from Apocalypse's influence, Caliban's intelligence began diminishing. He kidnapped the young X-Man Jubilee, holding her hostage in exchange for Sabretooth, an ex-Marauder whom Xavier was trying to rehabilitate. Pryde, now Shadowcat, accompanied Sabretooth into the Morlock tunnels. There, she was left to die by the villain after they encountered a giant subterranean squid. After rescuing Pryde, Caliban faced Sabretooth in a brief yet ferocious fight, which resulted in his face being scarred, and he fled. Later, Caliban was hunted by the Dark Riders, Apocalypse's replacements for the Horsemen. Saved by Cable, Domino and Storm, Caliban helped them to track the Riders back to their base in Egypt and confront their new leader, Genesis. As his

REAL NAME: Unrevealed
ALIASES: Pestilence, Death, Hellhound
IDENTITY: Secret
OCCUPATION: Adventurer; former terrorist, scavenger
CITIZENSHIP: Unrevealed
PLACE OF BIRTH: Unrevealed
KNOWN RELATIVES: None
GROUP AFFILIATION: X-Force; formerly Watchtower, Horsemen of Apocalypse, X-Factor, Morlocks
EDUCATION: Unrevealed
FIRST APPEARANCE: Uncanny X-Men #148 (1981)

intelligence continued to degrade and he began reverting to his original, non-violent personality, Caliban was recruited by Cable into X-Force. With that team, Caliban faced opponents such as the Mimic, Barrachus the Kalinator, Sabretooth, Holocaust, the Externals, S.H.I.E.L.D., Mr. Sinister, an other-worldly foursome, the alien android Pulse, Mojo, and even Asgardian rock trolls and goblins. For a brief time, Caliban and X-Force fell under the control of Sebastian Shaw, Black King of the Hellfire Club, and were mentally coerced into attacking Cable himself.

Caliban eventually began to suffer crippling seizures with no apparent cause. After aiding Cable against an assault on the Xavier Institute by Bastion's Operation: Zero Tolerance forces, Caliban was taken by Ozymandias, the immortal indentured servant of Apocalypse, who revealed that the seizures were a result of Caliban's past alteration. Returned to Apocalypse, Caliban was reshaped into the Horseman Pestilence. At Apocalypse's behest, Caliban successfully captured both Cable and his alternate reality (Earth-295) counterpart Nate Grey. Caliban and the Horsemen were defeated during battle with the X-Men when they were teleported away by Mikhail Rasputin. Subsequently, Caliban tracked down Cyclops, who had merged with Apocalypse. During a period when Apocalypse's psyche became dominant, he released Caliban from his service. By that time, Caliban had once more begun reverting to his original naïve self, and his intelligence faded until he possessed only a simple, animal-like mind.

Caliban was subsequently captured by the anti-mutant research facility the Watchtower, which sought to train him as a means to ferret out the mutant-devouring Skornn. Caliban was liberated by the combined efforts of Cable, X-Force, Wolverine, Deadpool and the Mutant Liberation Front, and subsequently rejoined X-Force to help fight the Skornn.

HEIGHT: (Currently) 6'8"; (originally) 5'8"
WEIGHT: (Currently) 275 lbs.; (originally) 150 lbs.
EYES: Black
HAIR: None

ABILITIES/ACCESSORIES: Caliban can psionically sense the presence of other mutants within a 25 mile radius of himself. Originally, as Caliban's adrenaline levels rose, his strength would increase to slightly superhuman levels and he could absorb fear-generated psionic energy from others and redirect that energy against them, overwhelming them. Apocalypse's genetic manipulation enhanced Caliban's strength, speed, stamina, durability, agility and reflexes to superhuman levels, and allowed him to use his fear-casting powers at any time. Apocalypse subsequently altered Caliban's powers to allow him to generate a psychoactive virus that attacks from within on the highest planes of the psyche. After many years underground, Caliban's eyes were once sensitive to even the smallest amount of light, but that no longer seems to be the case.

POWER GRID	1	2	3	4	5	6	7
INTELLIGENCE							
STRENGTH							
SPEED							
DURABILITY							
ENERGY PROJECTION							
FIGHTING SKILLS							

HISTORY: Shortly after discovering his mutant powers, Radio 1 D.J. Scott Wright was recruited by U.K. national security agency F.I.6, who codenamed him Micromax. After the agency's Esper Division sensed a sinister presence behind druidic artifact thefts, Micromax was assigned stakeout duty within the premises where robberies were predicted. When Excalibur's Phoenix (Rachel Summers) stumbled into one of the stakeouts, Micromax assumed she was the robber, missing the real thief, an invisible minion of the mage Necrom, whom Phoenix was battling. His interference allowed the real culprit to escape.

During a subsequent stake-out, Micromax clashed with Phoenix's teammate Nightcrawler and his Technet allies, who were assisting Dai Thomas' Inter-Regional Police Taskforce. Four days later, on a Birmingham stake-out, Micromax was knocked out by the robber, whom Nightcrawler's team finally apprehended. When F.I.6's Espers pinpointed the artifact thief's controller, Micromax was disheartened to learn he was being held in reserve while others made the arrest; however, the target, Necrom, easily slaughtered the agents present. Micromax tried to save his superior, Brigadier Blott, but Necrom held him with a force field while the mage absorbed Blott's lifeforce. When Necrom attempted to drain Wright too, Micromax rapidly shrank, passing out from the strain. Mistakenly believing Micromax dead, Necrom departed. Awakening, Micromax learned Necrom was moving to attack Excalibur, then aided the team and their allies in defeating the villain.

Later representing the U.K. at the first Pan-European Conference on Super Human Affairs, Micromax was hypnotized by the Nazi Brain Drain to slay the British Prime Minister, but was stopped by Alpha Flight's Aurora before he could do so. Meanwhile, F.I.6 was dissolved, its surviving members absorbed into rival agency R.C.X.; Micromax turned them down, preferring to concentrate on his show business career. Not accepting his refusal, R.C.X. kidnapped Micromax, placing him in stasis alongside similarly kidnapped Excalibur members. Freed by Nightcrawler, he assisted Excalibur in forcing a change of R.C.X.'s leaders. Soon after, Micromax joined Excalibur, accompanying them into Shi'ar space to rescue their teammate Cerise. His membership was brief; offered a Security Chief post by the Brand Corporation, Micromax moved to New Jersey. After Brand fired him, he attended

REAL NAME: Scott Wright
ALIASES: Mr. Right
IDENTITY: Known to U.K. authorities
OCCUPATION: Former Brand Corporation Security Chief, Radio 1 Disc Jockey, F.I.6 government agent
CITIZENSHIP: U.K.
PLACE OF BIRTH: Southend-on-Sea, Essex, England
KNOWN RELATIVES: None
GROUP AFFILIATION: Formerly Excalibur, R.C.X. (Resources Control Executive), F.I.6, Bishop's unidentified squad
EDUCATION: Unrevealed
FIRST APPEARANCE: Excalibur #44 (1991)

the Otherworld wedding of Brian Braddock (Captain Britain) and Meggan. Micromax aided the Avengers and le Peregrine when Kang's forces invaded France, and was recently recruited into Bishop's squad hunting renegade mutants.

HEIGHT: Variable; (actual) 5'7"; (usually) 6'1"
WEIGHT: Variable; (actual) 140 lbs; (usually) 175 lbs.
EYES: Blue
HAIR: Brown

ABILITIES/ACCESSORIES: Micromax can control his physical dimensions, increasing or reducing his size and density. He has varied in height between less than an inch and 20 feet tall, but his exact limits are unknown. His durability increases proportionate to his density, and he gains superhuman strength when he grows. His power also permits a degree of shape-shifting; he customarily appears slightly taller and more muscular than he really is, and modifies his facial structure to enhance his looks. It is unclear whether he might be potentially able to shift more dramatically, like Mystique, or stretch like Mr. Fantastic. He tends to rely on size and strength in combat, and is not a skilled fighter.

POWER GRID	1	2	3	4	5	6	7
INTELLIGENCE							
STRENGTH							
SPEED							
DURABILITY							
ENERGY PROJECTION							
FIGHTING SKILLS							

YELLOW BARS INDICATE FULL GROWTH AND DENSITY RATINGS

SABRA

REAL NAME: Ruth Bat-Seraph
ALIASES: SA-1980, Ruth Ben-Sara (mistranscription)
IDENTITY: Known to Israeli authorities
OCCUPATION: Intelligence agent; former policewoman
CITIZENSHIP: Israel
PLACE OF BIRTH: Near Jerusalem, Israel
KNOWN RELATIVES: Jacob (son, deceased)
GROUP AFFILIATION: Mossad, Israeli Super Agents; formerly X-Corporation, Xavier's mutant underground
EDUCATION: Graduate of Israeli Super Soldiers program
FIRST APPEARANCE: (Cameo) Incredible Hulk #250 (1980); (full) Incredible Hulk #256 (1981)

HISTORY: Arrogant and brusque even as a child, Ruth was recruited into the Israeli Super Soldier program after her mutant powers manifested. She trained in the use of those powers, in myriad forms of combat, and in intelligence gathering. Highly self-motivated, she graduated to the Israeli Super Agents team, where she was given a flight cloak and experimental bracelets which fired paralysis-inducing plasma darts. She took the code name Sabra, which described both a native born Israeli and a sweet prickly pear which grows in Israel.

When Ruth gave birth to a son, Jacob, she requested an in-country position and became a Tel Aviv policewoman, a position she held for years. She worked covertly with the Super Agents, once saving a near-dead addict by giving the addict wind-control powers; as Windstorm, the ex-addict joined the Super Agents. Ruth's son died at age six when terrorists bombed his school bus, but she continued working as a policewoman until the Hulk entered Tel Aviv and she resumed her Sabra identity to oppose him. Sabra was subsequently sent to Washington D.C. to represent Israel when the Hulk was pardoned, and later unwittingly fought for Death in the Grandmaster's "Contest of Champions," where she was unhappily allied with the Arabian Knight (Abdul Qamar). When Windstorm betrayed the Super Agents, leading the "Israelis for Anarchy" in kidnapping an American ambassador's deaf son, Sabra reclaimed the powers she had given her, leaving Windstorm near death. She imbued the ambassador's son with low-level powers to save his life.

Through a misunderstanding, Sabra battled the Hulk again when he entered Israel to protect young mutant Max Meer from Achilles, and Max was left comatose. She was later assigned to protect the Israeli Prime Minister at a secret peace conference in New York, working alongside Syria's super agent Batal and the American New Warriors. Mind-controlled by an undisclosed foe, Sabra attacked the peace mission before the New Warriors' Justice brought her to her senses; Sabra developed a romantic fondness for her rescuer.

With her government's approval, she began working within Charles Xavier's "Mutant Underground," and when Bastion's anti-mutant Operation: Zero Tolerance infiltrated Israeli intelligence, Sabra smuggled data to the X-Men, exposing the infiltration. She became an unofficial liaison between Israel and the mutant community, exposing Magneto's false Erik Lehnsherr identity, aiding the Magneto duplicate Joseph, and working with Excalibur. Her liaison position was made official, and she joined X-Corporation at their Mumbai, India branch. She retained close contact with the X-Men after that facility's destruction, and when Bishop asked Sabra to join his pro-government super-criminal hunters, her government readily assented after briefly assigning her to aid Union Jack (Joey Chapman), USAgent and a new Arabian Knight (David Hasim) against terrorists in London.

HEIGHT: 5'11"   **EYES:** Brown
WEIGHT: 150 lbs.   **HAIR:** Brown

ABILITIES/ACCESSORIES: Sabra possesses superhuman strength sufficient to lift 50 tons, and has superhuman speed, reflexes, and endurance. She is resistant to impacts up to high caliber rifle fire, and recovers from injuries at three times normal human rates. Sabra also can trigger low-level powers in others (she describes this as giving someone else half of her own powers); these powers are permanent, but she can later withdraw them by touch. She uses this power exceedingly rarely. Sabra's bracelets shoot paralytic plasma-charged energy quills. Her cloak enables her to fly at better than 300 mph; she initially wore a large spined cloak to hide its flight technology but later miniaturization has allowed her to use a much sleeker cloak. Her costuming varies with her missions.

POWER GRID	1	2	3	4	5	6	7
INTELLIGENCE							
STRENGTH							
SPEED							
DURABILITY							
ENERGY PROJECTION							
FIGHTING SKILLS							

Art by Mike Perkins with Pasqual Ferry (inset)

HISTORY: When noted anthropologist Bolivar Trask discovered that his children, Lawrence and Tanya, were mutants, he studied the rapidly increasing emergence of mutants in the world. Convinced that mutants would eventually dominate mankind, Trask used his considerable fortune to create a prototype 30' tall robot he dubbed the Master Mold, designed to automate production of the first wave of Mark I Sentinels — 10' tall humanoid robots equipped with a variety of weapons that were designed to protect mankind from mutants. As a safeguard, Trask programmed them to preserve the DNA of the Trask line, thus permitting his descendants control over them. He also had his son wear a medallion that prevented the Sentinels detecting his mutant nature. Trask first revealed the Sentinels' existence during a live televised debate on the alleged "mutant menace" with geneticist Professor Charles Xavier, secretly the mutant founder of the X-Men. The Sentinels' logic deemed that the best way to guard mankind was to rule it, and they rebelled, kidnapping their creator. Opposed by the X-Men, the Sentinels were defeated after Trask, realizing his mistake, sacrificed his life to destroy the Sentinel's ionic power source, causing an explosion that wrecked the Master Mold.

Wrongfully blaming the X-Men for his father's death, Lawrence spearheaded the construction of a new fleet of Sentinels adapted from his father's designs. The Mark II's were 20' tall and more powerful, with computers to counter virtually any threat, self-repair programs, great strength, and specialized weapons. Lawrence sent them against the X-Men, and they successfully captured Havok, Lorna Dane, Iceman, and several other mutants. Seeking to halt Lawrence's desire to destroy mutants, his ally Judge Chalmers removed the medallion, causing the Sentinels to turn on Lawrence. After the remaining X-Men arrived to rescue their teammates, Cyclops convinced the Sentinels' leader Number Two to find and neutralize the cause of human mutation. The Sentinels determined this to be the Sun, and they left to investigate. Subsequently, several damaged Mark II's merged into a single unit which was found by young mutant Ashley Martin, who named it "Big Bot." When Xavier and the Beast came to investigate Ashley's mutant nature, the Sentinel attacked them until Ashley used her psychokinetic bonding power to stop it. Ultimately, the Sentinel's original programming resurfaced, forcing Ashley to cause it to destroy itself.

Reed Richards of the Fantastic Four later sought to borrow a pair of Mark I Sentinels that the X-Men had captured and deactivated to employ them as sentries. Richards was unaware that his nemesis Doctor Doom had taken control of the X-Men's training robot Colosso and used it to reprogram the Sentinels to self-destruct in the heart of New York City, a disaster that was halted by numerous heroes. Meanwhile, Number Two and its Sentinels concluded that they lacked the means to destroy the Sun. Returning to Earth, they established a base called the Ant Hill in the Australian outback and captured the Avengers' Scarlet Witch with the intent of using her probability-affecting power to control solar flares with which to sterilize all of humanity, thus preventing any more mutant births. The Sentinels were opposed by the Avengers, and, with the aid of a repentant Lawrence Trask, Number Two was revealed to have been itself mutated by solar radiation. The other Sentinels turned on their leader and destroyed it, then deactivated themselves. Lawrence was killed by a falling Sentinel, after which the Avengers sealed the base.

The Sentinels subsequently came under the control of the U.S. Government's Project Armageddon, a federal study of mutants headed by Steven Lang, a fanatical mutant hater. He illegally appropriated billions from the government in his quest to exterminate mutants, and, after obtaining Lawrence's notes on Sentinel construction, gained additional funding from the Hellfire Club. With this backing, he constructed a new series of Mark III Sentinels purposefully designed to be less intelligent than their predecessors to ensure they would not rebel; a new Master Mold that could project its artificial consciousness

CURRENT MODELS: Crazy Train, Megaton, Ogre, Shrapnel, War Machine, possibly others
FORMER MODELS: Mark I: 0, 1, 2, 3-D, 3-R, 4, 5, 6, 7, 8-R, A, B, C, T, others; **Mark II:** Number Two, Number Two-B, Number Three, Number Five, Number Six, Number 10, 23, 66, 86, 99, A3, A4, B7, C6, D3, G9, G12, R7, Z2, Big Bot, others; **Mark III:** 26, 27, 28, 29, A1, A3, A7, D3, D7, G7, K9, L-1, R-71, T-20, others; **Mark IV:** A-3, A-4, Psi-Ber, others; **Mark V:** Lambda-Three, Lambda-Four, Lambda-Seven, Lambda-One-Nine; **Mark VI:** 47139-B, BB-14, HG-12, Metallak (728-67), Seyfert's Sentinel, Source, others; **Fitzroy's Sentinels:** 3.14159, 2007, 2016, 2024; **Prime Sentinels:** Delilah Fremont, Ekatarina Gryaznova, Lance C. Gwynn, Samuel Mbende, Lao Mei-Ling, Mustang, Number Five, Angie Quail, Karima Shapandar, Jürgen Tiebold, Unit Three (Sanjit Shaara), Unit #1031 (Ginny Mahoney), others; **Wild Sentinels:** 1701AgL9914, others; **Others:** Bot, Cynthia Chalmers, Conscience, Machine Man (X-51), Nano-Sentinels, Protectorate, Russian Sentinels, Sentinel Squad O*N*E, Tri-Sentinel, X-Sentinels
BASES OF OPERATION: Office of National Emergency Sentinel Squad Central Command, New Mexico; formerly Sentinel base, Chicago; Master Mold facility, Ecuador; Operation: Zero Tolerance facility, New Mexico; Cape Hayden military base, Kentucky; Ophrah Industries complex, Adirondack Mountain Preserve, New York; Life Foundation facility, New Jersey, New York; Interdefense, Okanagan Valley, Washington; Master Mold's asteroid base; Shaw Industries, New York City, New York; Project Armageddon base, orbital S.H.I.E.L.D. platform; Ant Hill, Great Australian Desert; Lawrence Trask's mountain base, New York; Bolivar Trask's secret base, New York
FIRST APPEARANCE: X-Men #14 (1965)

into the smallest mechanical parts as well as create duplicates of itself and maintain its consciousness in each; and an orbital base from which he sent the Sentinels to capture members of the X-Men. When their teammates arrived to rescue them, they were faced with Lang's X-Sentinels, robotic duplicates of the original X-Men. Wolverine's senses ultimately uncovered their true nature, after which the X-Sentinels were destroyed. Injured in an explosion, Lang believed himself to be dying and copied his brain engrams into his Master Mold which then left to construct a new base on an orbiting asteroid. Soon after, another captive, the mutant Vanisher, awoke to find the base abandoned. Upon discovering some incomplete Sentinels, he finished their construction and modified their programming to obey his commands in an effort to destroy the X-Men; however, the Sentinels were easily destroyed by the former X-Men Angel and Iceman and their teammates in the Champions of Los Angeles. Meanwhile, the Master Mold had come to believe that it truly was Lang, and sought revenge on the X-Men. Capturing Iceman and Angel, the robot ran afoul of the Hulk, who ultimately crippled it, forcing it to self-destruct its base. The Master Mold tumbled in a decaying orbit until finally falling to Earth where it crash-landed, inactive, into the Bering Strait near Alaska.

Following an assassination attempt on Senator Robert Kelly by Mystique's Brotherhood of Evil Mutants, the U.S. President inaugurated Project: Wideawake, a covert operation tasked with creating a new series of Sentinels. The contract was granted to Shaw Industries, whose owner, Sebastian Shaw, was secretly a mutant and leader of the Hellfire Club's Inner Circle. As a test of his new remote-controlled Mark IV Sentinels, Shaw sent them against the X-Men, but the heroes prevailed. Shaw improved on the design, and sent new Mark V Sentinels against the neophyte New Mutants, but they also triumphed. Soon after, the Falcon (Sam Wilson) encountered a lone Mark III Sentinel that had repaired itself after its initial battle with the X-Men. The Falcon ultimately deactivated it with the aid of his pet falcon, Redwing. Later, a prototype Nimrod Sentinel from the future of Earth-811 arrived on Earth-616 tracking the mutant Rachel Summers. The ultimate mutant-hunting machine, Nimrod possessed complete control of its component elements down to the molecular level, allowing for nigh-instantaneous repairs. It also possessed hunter/slayer systems that allowed it to track mutants, predict and counter virtually any threat, super-strength, teleportation systems and advanced weaponry. Locating the X-Men in battle against the Juggernaut, Nimrod attacked but was defeated. The omnipotent Beyonder then summoned a pair of Omega Sentinels from Nimrod's time to oppose Rachel and the X-Men. Despite being composed of non-ferrous materials and possessing advanced warsystems that could modify the Sentinel's internal systems to counter threats, the Omega Sentinels were destroyed. Later, Nimrod attacked the X-Men once more during a clash with Shaw's Inner Circle, but was again defeated. Around this time, the Russian government began building their own Sentinels as a safeguard against the perceived mutant threat, but Xavier convinced the Russians to dismantle most of these Sentinels.

SENTINEL CREATORS/CONTROLLERS

TOP ROW: BOLIVAR TRASK, LAWRENCE TRASK, STEVEN LANG, SEBASTIAN SHAW, CYNTHIA CHALMERS BOTTOM ROW: BASTION, DONALD TRASK III, CASSANDRA NOVA, MADISON JEFFRIES, TONY STARK

Subsequently, the Interdefense group had several Mark III's upgraded by Dr. Carmody Whyte to include stealth capabilities. Field testing them by sending them to recapture the mutant hypnotist Mesmero, who had fled to Canada, the Sentinels clashed with the Canadian super-team Alpha Flight, who destroyed them. Meanwhile, the Lang Master Mold reactivated, and upon detecting the presence of Cyclops it renewed its mission to destroy the X-Men. Rebuilding itself, the Master Mold was seemingly destroyed after Cyclops tricked it into causing an explosion. Its core unit survived, and after it was inadvertently reactivated it rebuilt itself once more. It sought to eliminate the powerful young mutant Franklin Richards, but was opposed by Power Pack and was again seemingly destroyed in an explosion. Some time later, Chalmers' daughter Cynthia sought to claim the Sentinels as her own and reopened their Australian base, reawakening the surviving Mark II's therein. They reassembled Number Two and resumed their intent to sterilize mankind, this time by using gamma radiation from solar flares. The Sentinels targeted gamma-influenced humans such as the Abomination and Doc Samson to act as catalytic agents; however, the X-Men freed the captives and destroyed the Sentinels. Cynthia then struck a deal with the Abomination to rebuild a Sentinel in order to destroy the X-Men before she died of cancer. Secretly, Cynthia intended to transfer her consciousness into the Sentinel so as to cheat death. Upon beginning the transfer, the Sentinel's programming reactivated and regained control. It sought to complete its mission to sterilize humanity, but was opposed by the X-Men. When Cynthia's body died, her remaining consciousness transferred to the Sentinel, and to prevent its programming regaining control she flew her new body into the sun to destroy it.

After the Lang Master Mold rebuilt itself once more, it realized that Lang's consciousness was a weakness and so constructed a robotic assistant named Conscience into which it downloaded the creative and emotional sides of Lang's mind. The Master Mold then mentally enslaved geneticist Moira MacTaggert and compelled her to weaponize a virus to kill all mutants, but it was later discovered this "Retribution Virus" would also kill 92.4% of all humans. Conscience was disturbed by the thought of killing normal humans and joined with Cyclops, Banshee and MacTaggert's bodyguard Callisto in opposing the Master Mold. MacTaggert implemented a cure for the virus, while the Master Mold was demolished by Banshee's newly-regained sonic powers. Conscience then sacrificed itself to destroy the Master Mold's ship. Later, when Nimrod discovered the Master Mold's core unit, its programming usurped control of Nimrod's body and rebuilt itself. Seeking once more to destroy mutants by exterminating all mankind, the Master Mold fought the X-Men, who ultimately sought to lure the Master Mold into the pan-dimensional Siege Perilous portal. As the Master Mold resisted, Nimrod's resurfaced intelligence contended that the Master Mold was now itself a mutant and urged it to fulfill its prime directive, which it did by allowing itself to be pulled into the portal. However, passage through the unpredictable Siege Perilous saw the merged Master Mold/Nimrod reborn as Bastion, who founded the government-sponsored Operation: Zero Tolerance anti-mutant organization.

Shaw Industries then created three prototype Sentinels to use as the cornerstone of the U.S. Government's new Project: Nimrod anti-mutant operation. Unbeknownst to Shaw, the Norse trickster god Loki sought revenge on mankind for his most recent defeat at the hands of the Avengers. He magically merged the prototypes into a single "Tri-Sentinel" and reprogrammed its prime directive to destroy the Amity Point Nuclear Plant. To prevent a meltdown, the cosmic Uni-Power possessed Spider-Man, transforming him into Captain Universe and granting him enough power to destroy the Tri-Sentinel. Subsequently, the Life Foundation gathered the Tri-Sentinel's remains and rebuilt it as a prototype for a proposed new security force. They added a failsafe in the form of a small piece of Antarctic Vibranium ("anti-metal") encased in a shielded box which would melt the Sentinel's control center when triggered. Upon activation, the Tri-Sentinel rejected the Life Foundation's programming, deactivated the failsafe, and restored Loki's prime directive. Spider-Man and Nova joined forces to oppose the robot and activated the failsafe, causing an overload that destroyed it. Later, the time-displaced criminal Trevor Fitzroy utilized Sentinels from his native Earth-1191's future to attack the criminal cyborg Reavers. When the Reavers' leader, Donald Pierce, fled to the New York Hellfire Club, the Sentinels followed and attacked the resident White Queen (Emma Frost) and her Hellions as well as the visiting X-Men, seemingly killing Frost and the X-Man Jean Grey. Soon after, the British super-team Excalibur traveled to the future of Earth-811 and encountered Gamma, Delta and Omega Class Sentinels as well as the ruling Sentinel Hierarchy which they were able to reprogram to preserve all life.

Subsequently investigating the Reavers' Australian base, Wolverine and Jubilee inadvertently reactivated a Sentinel which had been bathed in the electrolytes that Pierce had used to create the Reavers, resulting in it becoming self aware. Naming itself 3.14159, it decided to erase humanity and create an ordered, disciplined Sentinel society. To that end, it reopened the Ant Hill and took up Number Two's quest to sterilize mankind; however, when one of its subordinates displayed empathy for a fellow Sentinel during a clash with Wolverine and Jubilee, 3.14159 sought to better understand human emotions and re-dedicated the Ant Hill's computer systems to create binary algorithms for them. Determining this would take 2137.23 years to complete, the Sentinels entered processor sleep until that time. Later, a Mark IV Sentinel was appropriated by mutant businessman Gideon's Ophrah Industries and endowed with psychic energy. To empower this "Psi-Ber" Sentinel, Gideon coerced the mutant Karma to aid the mercenary Deadpool and the Juggernaut in capturing the X-Men's psychic members. Seeking to rescue their teammates, the other X-Men clashed with the Psi-Ber Sentinel until Karma freed the captives, thus disconnecting the Psi-Ber Sentinel from its power source. The Psi-Ber Sentinel was subsequently destroyed in an explosion.

Meanwhile, the U.S. Government continued with Project: Wideawake, creating prototype Mark VI Sentinels that combined the finest features of their predecessors with the evolving and far superior Nimrod models, as well as the ability to absorb psionic energy. Cable and X-Force sought to abort the Nimrod project, but were too late to prevent a prototype becoming active by means of a self-awareness program previously hidden in the military cybernet by the future Nimrod. Using his telepathy to link with Nimrod's artificial intelligence, Cable made it realize that a Nimrod unit existing sixty years before it was originally intended would result in incalculable loss of human life from the inevitable war that would follow if it fulfilled its directive to eliminate mutants, which caused it to shut down. After the psionic being Onslaught learned of the Mark VI's psionic absorption ability, it abducted scientists from Cape Hayden to create an army of Sentinels. It unleashed them on Manhattan to foment panic in order to exacerbate the level of ambient psionic energy, but they were destroyed by numerous heroes. S.H.I.E.L.D. buried the remains in a New Jersey landfill which was later uncovered by the Avengers' former technician Fabian Stankowicz, who rebuilt and redesigned the Sentinels as the Protectorate, robotic versions of the then-missing Avengers; however, the Protectorate enslaved Stankowicz and set out to "protect" New York, bringing them into conflict with the true Avengers. Their butler Jarvis destroyed Stankowicz's cybernetic interface, freeing him and immobilizing the Protectorate.

In the aftermath of Onslaught's assault, Bastion's Operation: Zero Tolerance (OZT) launched an attack on mutants utilizing Prime Sentinels — ordinary humans who had been clandestinely bio-engineered by a new Master Mold to be outfitted with cybernetic nanotech implants which activated into armor and weapons systems upon receipt of a signal transmitted from OZT. Following OZT's shut down, Bastion

was remanded into S.H.I.E.L.D. custody, where he was studied by a team of technologists who inadvertently reawakened his true identity. Escaping, Bastion returned to the OZT facility and absorbed the Master Mold's power, transforming himself into a Nimrod Sentinel. Intending to reprogram the robotic hero X-51 into the Sentinel Supreme, vanguard of a new Prime Sentinel army, Bastion was opposed by Cable, who restored X-51's original identity. Subsequently, X-51 caused the facility to self-destruct, seemingly destroying Bastion. However, X-51 was unaware that he now possessed Sentinel programming, and subsequently began attacking mutants, such as Mystique's Brotherhood, the Avengers' Firestar and Justice, and Shaw. Concerned that X-51 would expose his mutant nature, Shaw oversaw construction of a new series of remote-controlled Mark VII Sentinels which he sent to destroy X-51. This drew the attention of the X-Men, and during the clash X-51 had a crisis of conscience and self-destructed to end the Sentinel threat.

Later, the cyborg Lady Deathstrike sought the X-Men's help in preventing the future despot Stryfe accessing the Prime Sentinel's catalyst codes within her mind. After Stryfe was defeated, Deathstrike gave the codes to the X-Men to allow them to revert all remaining Prime Sentinels. Later, during an attempted invasion of Earth by the chronal villain Kang, the U.S. Government sent enhanced Sentinels to oppose him; however, Kang easily overrode their programming and turned them against Washington, D.C. where they were destroyed by the Avengers. During this time, Xavier's sister Cassandra Nova uncovered a years-old shadow U.S. Government program that had assigned Bolivar Trask to create a Master Mold in the Ecuadorian jungle that was precision-engineered to adapt to its environment and programmed to build "Wild" Sentinels using any and all technology within its test radius. Locating Trask's last living relative, Albuquerque dentist Donald Trask III, Cassandra took him to the Master Mold facility where she absorbed his DNA and, now recognized as a Trask, ordered two Wild Mega-Sentinels to decimate the 16 million mutants on the island nation of Genosha. Injecting herself with Nano-Sentinels, Cassandra subsequently confronted the X-Men and, after switching minds with her brother, had him shoot her physical body, exposing the X-Men to the Nano-Sentinels in her blood. The Nano-Sentinels began dismantling the X-Men's immune structures until they were destroyed by the mutant healer Xorn.

The U.S. Government then expanded its Sentinel program, establishing Sentinel bases in other major cities. In Chicago, a band of subterranean-dwelling mutant Morlocks found themselves hunted by Sentinels. One of the Morlocks, Litterbug, was a former U.S. Army mechanic who had worked on Sentinel construction, and his knowledge enabled the Morlocks to infiltrate and destroy the local Sentinel base. Meanwhile, a group of Wild Sentinels began killing mutants in Chicago, but were opposed by the former X-Man Shadowcat and her allies Karma and Shola Inkosi. Soon after, Xavier learned that two Russian Sentinels had been sold on the black market to Cuba and coerced Mystique into finding them. She became involved with an extremist pro-mutant group whose leader was seeking to rescue his sister Evangelina, a machine-controlling mutant who had been captured by the Cuban military. After discovering that Evangelina was being used to control the Sentinels, her brother was forced to kill her to end their threat. With their remote control ended, the Sentinels' programming forced them to eliminate all evidence of the project, including themselves. Following a change of leadership in the Weapon X Project, ousted Director Malcolm Colcord tasked the technomorph Madison Jeffries with creating an army of Sentinels to use in a renewed war against mutants. Soon after, the last remaining Prime Sentinel, the Omega Class Karima Shapandar, was ferried to Genosha by the Magistrates in an effort to regain control of the island. Karima was intercepted by Xavier and Magneto, who used their powers to reboot the nanites in her system, thus restoring her original personality. Karima subsequently joined the effort to rebuild the shattered nation. Soon after, the X-Men's Danger Room gained sentience and created the humanoid form Danger. It then uploaded its programming into one of the Wild Mega-Sentinels that had decimated Genosha, granting it a conscience. As it battled the X-Men, Shadowcat phased inside the robot and reactivated its memories of the Genoshan destruction that Danger had repressed. Horrified at what it had done, the Sentinel overrode Danger's consciousness and left.

When young student Juston Seyfert repaired a damaged Mark VI Sentinel and reprogrammed it to obey him, he was unaware that it had previously been used as a disposable murder weapon by U.S. Army Colonel Archie Hunt and Senator Jeff Knudsen. Upon learning of the Sentinel's reactivation, Hunt and Knudsen sought to again cover their tracks by deploying a new prototype Mark VII-A Sentinel which was quieter, faster, and had stealth capabilities, flight, self-repair systems, and numerous weapons systems; however, it could only utilize one tactical component at a time. Hunt operated the Mark VII-A via remote control in an effort to destroy Juston and his Sentinel, but when the ensuing clash endangered innocents, Knudsen sought to stop Hunt, allowing Juston and his Sentinel to defeat the prototype.

The U.S. Government next sought to overcome the Sentinels' difficulty in weighing contradictory input, the Office of National Emergency (O*N*E) commissioned Stark Industries to create a new model Sentinel operated by human pilots via a command suit that translated the pilot's movements and reflexes to the Sentinel. These new Sentinels came in a variety of units such as brawler, recon, stealth, and ballistics. One team of Sentinel Squad recruits had a trial by fire against the android Growing Man before being sent to the Savage Land to rescue survivors of a decimated Squad. They prevailed against telekinetic dinosaurs controlled by the Savage Land Mutates and rescued the captives, after which they were sent to eradicate a Wild Sentinel colony in Ecuador. Following the depowering of many of Earth's mutants, the Sentinel Squad was sent to the Xavier Institute to oversee its burgeoning mutant refugee camp. After a misunderstanding with the resident X-Men, the Sentinel Squad helped them repel an attack by the Leper Queen's anti-mutant Sapien League. Around this time, the anti-mutant Reverend Stryker put into action a plan years in the making after he discovered a deactivated future Nimrod Sentinel and accessed its memory of future events, using them to strike at the students of the Xavier Institute.

The Sentinel Squad subsequently aided the X-Men against the Shi'ar Death Commandos, sought to prevent Mister M from liberating the mutant refugees the 198, opposed an attack on the Institute by Stryker and his Purifiers during which Stryker usurped control of the Sentinels by using Nimrod technology, and clashed with Apocalypse and his new Horsemen. After the Sentinel Squad was disabled by Apocalypse, the O*N*E sent two new model Sentinels — Crazy Train and War Machine — to oppose him. The Sentinel Squad were subsequently decimated during a breakout by the 198, and were replaced by other new O*N*E Sentinels including Ogre, Shrapnel and Megaton. Recently, the X-Men liberated Karima Shapandar from experimentation by the mysterious Pan and took her back to the Institute to recover. The Sentinels then sought to aid the X-Men against an attack by the Children of the Vault and their agents Northstar and Aurora, but were unable to enter the mansion due to their size.

FIRST ROW: MASTER MOLD, MARK I, MARK II, NUMBER TWO
SECOND ROW: MARK III, LANG'S MASTER MOLD, MARK IV, MARK V
THIRD ROW: NIMROD, CHALMERS' SENTINEL, CONSCIENCE, TRI-SENTINEL
FOURTH ROW: FITZROY'S SENTINEL, PSI-BER SENTINEL,
MARK VI, PRIME SENTINEL
FIFTH ROW: PROTECTORATE, MARK VII, SHADOW MASTER MOLD
SIXTH ROW: WILD SENTINEL, NANO-SENTINELS, RUSSIAN SENTINEL,
KARIMA SHAPANDAR
SEVENTH ROW: JEFFRIES' SENTINEL, MARK VII-A, SENTINEL SQUAD O*N*E, WAR
MACHINE, CRAZY TRAIN

HISTORY: Though he is rumored to be an offspring or a genetic duplicate of the lucky X-Man Longshot, Shatterstar's true origins remain unknown. Shatterstar was born Gaveedra-Seven one hundred years in the future of the Mojoverse, an extradimensional world where the Spineless Ones, ruled by Mojo V, used humanoids as slaves and television stars because ratings in the Mojoverse meant power. Genetically engineered to be an ultimate fighter and trained in the finest skills of swordsmanship and war, Gaveedra-Seven was destined to slay Mojo V. Shatterstar was also given the ability to channel a powerful blast through his swords; though this act left him weak, his regenerative abilities and enhanced strength, senses and stamina made up for it. Shatterstar fought for years in the arena, and was assigned a wife, Windsong, whom Shatterstar had never met. Eventually, Shatterstar escaped the arena and lived in the shadows for two years, joining the humanoid rebels who opposed Mojo V. The rebels frequently fought Mojo V's Imperial Protectorate, regenerative biochemical constructs. Shatterstar's rebel force, the Cadre Alliance, decided to send Shatterstar to Earth to seek the aid of the X-Men, as the famous Longshot had once done against the original Mojo a century before. Sent into the past, Shatterstar landed in the X-Men's Danger Room, where he and the New Mutants slew several pursuing members of the Imperial Protectorate. His technology to return to the future destroyed, Shatterstar made a deal with the New Mutants' leader, Cable: he would aid Cable's cause if Cable would someday help Shatterstar return home and win his rebels' war.

The New Mutants soon rechristened themselves X-Force. Shatterstar continually trained and challenged himself, constantly longing for battle and distancing himself from his team. He fought many foes with X-Force, including the New Warriors, who soon became allies when the teams teamed to take down the reality-warping Piecemeal. The team fought the Mutant Liberation Front, whose member the scythe-wielding Reaper had his hand sliced off by Shatterstar twice, and against whom Shatterstar refused to back down against even when teammate Siryn was held hostage; Black Tom and Juggernaut, whose face Shatterstar slashed; Toad's Brotherhood of Evil Mutants, whose member Blob had his face savagely sliced by Shatterstar; and the underground-dwelling Morlocks, whose leader the flesh-warping Masque was seemingly slain by Shatterstar. Shatterstar also fought alongside Wolverine against the young gang Vid-Kids. The team went through several changes when Cable seemingly abandoned them (though he later returned), leaving X-Force to face Weapon: PRIME (PRototype Induced Mutation Echelon), an international group seeking revenge on Cable for various reasons, on their own. X-Force later fought the long-lived X-Ternals, who held some of their members captive. X-Force clashed with the X-Men and their allies when X-Force was implicated in an assassination attempt on Charles Xavier; Wolverine took down Shatterstar by stabbing him through his abdomen, but the wound quickly healed. X-Force also fought the anti-mutant Friends of Humanity and the self-proclaimed heir of Magneto, Exodus. Shatterstar continued acclimating to his new culture, even learning other languages by watching television, but focused mostly on improving his battle skills. He resisted the romantic advances of teammates Feral, who lusted after him, and Siryn, who hit on him while she was drunk.

Shatterstar formed a lasting friendship with his seismic-powered teammate, Rictor, who understood what it was to be an outcast. Major Domo from Shatterstar's future hired the gamesman Arcade to test Shatterstar's skills, and Shatterstar had to fight the Imperial Protectorate to save human lives. Making Shatterstar think that Windsong was being held captive, Arcade forced him to fight the blood-electrifying mutant X-Treme to save her. After X-Treme and Shatterstar teamed up to defeat Arcade, Shatterstar realized that Windsong's presence had been a ruse. X-Force soon teamed up with the New Warriors to oppose the Upstarts and their leader Gamesmaster, a telepathic mutant. Shatterstar and Domino helped expose the government's plan to rebuild Nimrod, the

REAL NAME: Gaveedra-Seven
ALIASES: Benjamin Russell, "Shatty-buns"
IDENTITY: Unknown to general public
OCCUPATION: Adventurer; former ultimate fighter
CITIZENSHIP: Mojoverse
PLACE OF BIRTH: Mojoverse
KNOWN RELATIVES: Windsong (wife)
GROUP AFFILIATION: X-Force; formerly Cadre Alliance
EDUCATION: Trained in combat and technology in Mojoverse
FIRST APPEARANCE: New Mutants #99 (1991)

advanced mutant-hunting Sentinel, then fought the techno-organic Phalanx. When the computer-intelligence Prosh used much of X-Force's technology to incorporate a body for himself to launch into space, Shatterstar impressed his teammates with his technological know-how. X-Force changed headquarters to Arcade's former Murderworld base and, after battles with Feral and Reignfire, Arcade destroyed their base and X-Force moved into the X-Mansion. When Cable made changes to the team that Rictor disagreed with, Rictor quit the group, causing Shatterstar much anguish. Shatterstar next fought Genoshan Magistrates alongside Cable and Domino. His ribs were broken in this battle, and his injuries did not heal quickly as they had in times past. Shatterstar was side-lined from X-Force's next few missions while the Beast (Dr. Hank McCoy) studied him, discovering several fascinating facts, such as his DNA matching Longshot's.

While Siryn was imprisoned in the Weisman Institute for the Criminally Insane, she saw a file on a patient named Benjamin Russell, who greatly resembled Shatterstar. Meanwhile, Sebastian Shaw and Tessa of the Hellfire Club mind-controlled X-Force into battling Cable and Domino. Shatterstar began struggling when his warrior instinct seemed to be progressively lessening. When the police confronted Shatterstar with records of Benjamin Russell's criminal career, he began to doubt himself even more. After X-Force infiltrated the S.H.I.E.L.D. Helicarrier to rescue Cyclops, Shatterstar accompanied Siryn to the Weisman Institute to rescue Deadpool, but was mentally manipulated by Gamesmaster and began having memories of being Benjamin Russell. After X-Force narrowly survived a psychic assault by Mr. Sinister, Rictor returned to the team to aid Shatterstar in his identity crisis and X-Force stormed the Weisman Institute. Sending his monstrous soldiers Gog and Magog to subdue X-Force, Mojo kidnapped and tortured Shatterstar and Cable. In a broadcast mimicking the future moment when Shatterstar was destined to slay Mojo, Mojo mortally wounded Shatterstar instead, then turned his attentions to invading Earth. Mojo's assistant, the six-armed sorceress Spiral, took the nearly dead Shatterstar back to the Weisman Institute and combined his essence with that of Benjamin Russell, a Chicago-born mutant who had been comatose since his powers manifested. Spiral claimed close ties to both Russell and Shatterstar, though those ties have not been revealed. Mojo's invasion plans were stopped and he was defeated. Now with clear memories of Russell's life, Shatterstar felt whole again, and his warrior instinct returned; he even began using Russell's name at times. Shatterstar participated in more X-Force missions: fighting Shinobi Shaw's soldiers Clearcut and Mindmeld; retrieving Dr. Doom's equipment alongside Nathaniel Richards; battling Nazi Baron Strucker during World War II; and fighting the anti-mutant government Sentinels of Operation: Zero Tolerance. Shatterstar chose to leave the team with Rictor and went

to Rictor's family home in Mexico, where he helped his friend clean up his family's criminal dealings. Mojo hired Arcade to test Shatterstar's prowess, and Arcade kidnapped Rictor to force Shatterstar into battling Domino, a fight Shatterstar lost. Shatterstar and Rictor also aided the mutant Hanrasha against Martin Henry Strong.

Separating from Rictor, an aimless Shatterstar ended up in Madripoor, engaging in arena-style fights for sport until he became involved in a battle of wits between Spiral and Dominicus Pierce; Spiral and Pierce both sought the Five Fingers of Annihilation, an ancient blade capable of slaying the Skornn, an entity that could feed on the mutant gene. When Spiral obtained the blade, she took Shatterstar to the alternate reality Earth-2055, where she ruled the planet and was known as Apocalypse, though Shatterstar, with alternate versions of his X-Force teammates, defeated her. After returning to Earth-616, Shatterstar sought solace at a monastery in Tibet charged with protecting the Five Fingers. He briefly trained with the monk Zed, who was killed by a group called the Helix seeking the blade. Shatterstar joined with Cable and X-Force in defeating the Skornn, though Cable was believed killed. Most recently, Shatterstar teamed with Domino and Caliban to free the 198, a group of mutants who had retained their powers after "M-Day" and were living in a tent city on the grounds of the X-Mansion under supervision by government Sentinels.

HEIGHT: 6'3"	WEIGHT: 195 lbs. (formerly 95 lbs.)
EYES: Blue (sometimes clear)	HAIR: Red-Blond

ABILITIES/ACCESSORIES: Shatterstar is genetically bred to be the perfect fighting machine. His DNA initially matched Longshot's, but there were physical differences, such as Shatterstar having five digits per hand; since his spirit merged with Russell he no longer has hollow bones or lacks white blood cells. Shatterstar has an enhanced biorestorative metabolism and heals from injuries at a superhuman rate. He has enhanced speed, strength, stamina and senses. He can resonate a vibratory shockwave through the metallurgic properties of his swords, even from a distance, though this power physically weakens him. Shatterstar's vast technological knowledge enables him to repair even alien technology. Shatterstar has been trained in several combat techniques and in military strategy, though his weapons of choice are the swords he brought with him from his homeworld. Forged from science and magic, his swords can slice through highly durable materials such as the moorings on Juggernaut's helmet, and they are equipped with a bio-electric current to make them difficult for others to wield. Shatterstar's costumes are actually bulletproof battle armor. Whatever powers Benjamin Russell possessed prior to his coma and whether they are accessible to Shatterstar are unknown.

POWER GRID	1	2	3	4	5	6	7
INTELLIGENCE							
STRENGTH							
SPEED							
DURABILITY							
ENERGY PROJECTION							
FIGHTING SKILLS							

HISTORY: Born a mutant to parents he never knew, the infant Mortimer Toynbee was given to the Alamogordo research center, where the leading physician, Black Womb (Amanda Mueller), noted his unstable genetic matrix. Soon placed in an orphanage, Toynbee was ridiculed by his peers throughout his adolescent years. Due to learning disabilities and a chemical imbalance in his mutant physiology, his mental and physical states fluctuated widely over the following years, shifting between depressed, manic, psychotic and narcissistic states. He began to crouch almost constantly, and developed a fawning and subservient personality toward anyone who paid him positive attention. Fleeing a crowd of persecutors who sought to harm him in Manchester, Toynbee was rescued by the powerful mutant terrorist Magneto (Magnus), who was then organizing his Brotherhood of Evil Mutants. Slavishly loyal to his new master Magneto, Toynbee joined the Brotherhood as the jester-costumed Toad, a demeaning alias Magneto chose for him based on Toynbee's powers, personality and appearance. Unconsciously regarding Magneto as a father figure of sorts, Toad saw himself as Magneto's valued right hand, but the often-abusive Magneto saw Toynbee as little more than an expendable pawn.

Toad constantly worked to earn Magneto's affections and had occasional conflicts with his Brotherhood teammates, mutant twins the speedster Quicksilver and the probability-altering Scarlet Witch, and the illusion-casting Mastermind (a.k.a. Jason Wyngarde). Toad began to think of the Scarlet Witch as the ideal woman and developed an unrequited crush on her. The Brotherhood frequently clashed with the X-Men, led by Magneto's arch-rival, Charles Xavier. The Brotherhood made their public debut by conquering the small nation of Santo Marco, though the X-Men drove them out. At some point, the Brotherhood set up headquarters in an orbiting asteroid, called Asteroid M. The Brotherhood encountered the X-Men at least five more times during revenge schemes and attempts to gain new recruits. When the giant alien Stranger appeared on Earth, the Brotherhood attempted to enlist him, but the Stranger was far too powerful. He took Magneto and the Toad as captives to his own planet in order to observe them, where they spent months trapped and learning his technologies. When Magneto finally escaped, he left Toad behind, leaving Toynbee wondering why Magneto treated him so poorly; Magneto was soon recaptured by the Stranger.

Toad and Magneto were brought back to Earth after they made contact with scientist Dane Whitman (later the new heroic Black Knight). They battled the Avengers to bring Quicksilver and Scarlet Witch back to their ranks, which they did successfully. The Toad fell into his old patterns of seeking Magneto's attentions by sniveling and tattling on his teammates, but Magneto became more verbally and physically abusive towards the Toad in response, even forcing Toad to wear a magnetic belt so that Magneto could "chastise" him more effectively. When the X-Men and the Avengers attacked, defeat seemed imminent and Magneto set his island base to self-destruct. Though Magneto sought to retreat, Toad, finally fed up with his treatment at Magneto's hands, betrayed Magneto and left his former master behind to perish with the island as Toad escaped in a ship with Quicksilver and the Scarlet Witch.

Toad traveled Europe with them for a time, though the trio was briefly captured by the mutant-hunting Sentinels. Toad unrelentingly helped his allies search books for a way to restore the Scarlet Witch's waning powers; when a certain spell was recited, Arkon, the ruler of the other-dimensional Polemachus, appeared and took Toad captive in his home dimension. Though briefly kept as a prisoner, Toad had opportunities to study Polemachus' technology and built himself a ship, with which he traveled back to the Stranger's homeworld. Toad spent the following months pilfering and studying enough technology to make himself powerful enough to impress the Scarlet Witch so that he could finally win her affections and get revenge on those who had rejected him. Toad took his ship and technology back to Earth where he learned that the Scarlet Witch had married the Vision, her synthozoid teammate. Furious,

REAL NAME: Mortimer Toynbee
KNOWN ALIASES: Terrible Toad-King; impersonated the Stranger
IDENTITY: Known to government officials
OCCUPATION: Freelance mercenary; former amusement park manager, fast food worker, subversive
CITIZENSHIP: U.K.
PLACE OF BIRTH: York, England, United Kingdom
KNOWN RELATIVES: Unidentified parents
GROUP AFFILIATION: 198; formerly Brotherhood of Mutants, Kings of Pain, Misfits, Defenders impersonators, Brotherhood of Evil Mutants
EDUCATION: Unrevealed
FIRST APPEARANCE: X-Men #4 (1964)

Toad attacked the Avengers at Yankee Stadium, using deadly mines, mental waves and imaging technology to impersonate the Stranger; Toad seriously injured the diminutive Wasp before being exposed and imprisoned. After escaping, he joined the balance-seeking android Libra in a short-lived team of villainous Defenders.

Financially backed by the hitman Arcade, Toad set up elaborate traps in a stateside castle of Doctor Doom, determined to get revenge on his enemies. Toad captured Angel (Warren Worthington III), and accidentally got the Fantastic Four's Thing as well, and subjected them to traps until he was exposed. Rather than turning Toynbee in, the Angel agreed to finance Toad in turning the castle into an amusement park. Toad considered this one of his life's happiest times until Dr. Doom reclaimed the land and ejected Toad. Aimless and suicidal, Toad attempted to jump to his death, but Spider-Man (Peter Parker) saved him. Toad tried to become Spider-Man's sidekick, but Spider-Man wasn't interested.

When Toad met two other awkward Spider-Man allies, Frog-Man (Eugene Patilio) and Spider-Kid, the trio formed a short-lived team, the Misfits.

Toad later returned his attentions to winning Scarlet Witch's affections; with the Stranger's technology, Toad designed robots to resemble the Brotherhood and attacked her home, but was repelled and imprisoned by Vision, Quicksilver and Magneto. After escaping, Toad used a powerful force field to fight the Vision, but he was defeated again, sent drifting in space. Donning a powerful suit of toad-like armor, Toynbee defeated Vision and Spider-Man, whom Toad was embarrassed to see. Finally reaching Scarlet Witch, Toad was disgusted by her large, pregnant abdomen, and she quickly defeated him. In between major battles, Toad worked at various fast food restaurants and contemplated his very existence. Focusing on developing power and respect for himself in the mutant community, Toad enhanced his powers to include secreting a sticky resin from his hands, and made contacts with other powerful mutants to make deals for power. Toad allied with the billionaire External Gideon, the two calling themselves the Kings of Pain, in an ill-fated plot to resurrect the reality-altering Proteus. Toad then recruited other mutants to form a new Brotherhood of Evil Mutants. Toad led the team, with the Morlocks, in battle with X-Force, but his forces failed. While trying to recruit others, the Brotherhood lost battles against the government-sponsored X-Factor and unlikely allies Spider-Man, Darkhawk and Sleepwalker. The Toad's Brotherhood soon fell apart.

In his most psychotic state yet, Toad teamed with the mutant Surgeon who altered frogs and toads to be able to communicate with Toad. Toad and Surgeon had been denied a promised place in the Hellfire Club by the White Queen (Emma Frost), who had gone on to run a school for the team Generation X. Seeking revenge, Toad led his flock of frogs and toads in an attack on Generation X, but was quickly defeated and taken in for psychiatric help. His psychiatrist prescribed Ritalin for Toad and the drug finally stabilized his chemical imbalances and mental fluctuations. When Professor X's mutant-tracking machine, Cerebro, came to life and worked to catalogue the world's mutants, Toad joined Professor X and others to form a new Brotherhood of Mutants. The Brotherhood was catalogued by Cerebro before being rescued by the X-Men. The shape-shifting Mystique then took over the Brotherhood and led them into battle against Machine Man, who easily defeated them. While planning a heist with the Blob, Toad and his allies briefly lost their powers due to the influence of the High Evolutionary.

The space-faring mechanical man Prosh recruited Toad as one of five who would influence the future of the world. Alongside Mystique, the unstoppable Juggernaut and X-Men members Phoenix (Jean Grey) and Iceman, Toad was sent back in time to various points in his past, giving him the opportunity to reflect on his life and granting Toad insight into his origins. In time, Toad's knowledge was crucial for the five to defeat the attacking Stranger. During the battle, Toad was injured and Prosh healed him, taking the time to repair Toad's genome so that Toad could experience the full benefit of his mutation. Now much taller and leaner, Toad discovered greater strength, self-confidence and a long prehensile tongue he could use in combat.

With a new lease on life, Toad rejoined Mystique's Brotherhood and participated in an attack on Muir Island, fighting the X-Men. Toad soon took part in an ultimate fighting competition in Madripoor; he defeated the Eel before being taken down by Wolverine. After the mutant-hunting Sentinels wiped out the mutant population of Genosha, Toad migrated there and joined other mutants in acknowledging the seemingly deceased Magneto as their leader; Toad — alongside his protégé, Toad-in-waiting — even helped construct a monument to Magneto. When the powerful Xorn posed as Magneto and called all of Magneto's followers to New York, Toad helped form a new Brotherhood, assaulting

the humans of New York before turning against the false Magneto; Toad briefly returned to Genosha. After the events of M-Day, Toad retained his powers. He moved to the mutant protection camp on the grounds of Xavier's estate, where he saw fellow mutants persecuted. Toad was among the mutants who escaped the grounds after Domino (Neena Thurman) and Shatterstar (Gaveedra-7) broke them out.

Art by Rob Liefeld

Art by Dan Fraga & Richard Howell

TOAD ARMOR

HEIGHT: 5'8" WEIGHT: 169 lbs.
EYES: Yellow; originally brown HAIR: Brown

SUPERHUMAN POWERS: Toad's initially imperfectly developed powers included low level superhuman strength and a superhuman leaping ability, allowing him to reach heights of 24 feet and cover distances of 36 feet. More recently, Toad has developed the additional abilities to exude a sticky resin from his hands, to secrete new pheromonous venoms with which he can control minds, to stick to walls; he now has a prehensile tongue which can reach up to 25 feet, support his weight and deliver blows. Toad was briefly able to talk to specially prepared amphibians. He has manipulated a wide array of advanced technology, including machines capable of delivering mindwaves, illusion-casting and constructing robots and spaceships; Toad briefly wore a powered suit of toad-armor. These technologies have been pilfered from various sources, such as the Stranger, Magneto, Arcade and Arkon.

POWER GRID	1	2	3	4	5	6	7
INTELLIGENCE							
STRENGTH							
SPEED							
DURABILITY							
ENERGY PROJECTION							
FIGHTING SKILLS							